EXPERIENCING
GOD SERIES

D0201777

DISCOVERING GOD'S WILL

WARREN AND RUTH MYERS

NAVPRESS

A MINISTRY OF THE NAVIGATORS
P.O. BOX 6000, COLORADO SPRINGS, CO 80934

The Navigators is an international Christian organization. Jesus Christ gave His followers the Great Commission to go and make disciples (Matthew 28:19). The aim of The Navigators is to help fulfill that commission by multiplying laborers for Christ in every nation.

NavPress is the publishing ministry of The Navigators. NavPress publications are tools to help Christians grow. Although publications alone cannot make disciples or change lives, they can help believers learn biblical discipleship, and apply what they learn to their lives and ministries.

© 1980 by The Navigators
All rights reserved, including translation
ISBN: 0-89109-050-9
10504

Tenth printing, 1987

Unless otherwise noted, all Bible quotations are from the *New American Standard Bible* (NASB), © The Lockman Foundation 1960, 1962, 1963, 1968, 1971, 1972, 1973, 1975, 1977. Other versions quoted are *The Amplified Bible* (AMP), © 1965 by Zondervan Publishing House; *The Living Bible* (LB), © 1971 by Tyndale House Publishers, Wheaton, Illinois, used by permission; *The Modern Language Bible: The Berkeley Version in Modern English* (BERK), © 1945, 1959, 1969 by Zondervan Publishing House; *The New Testament, A New Translation by James Moffatt* (MOF), © 1964 by James Moffatt, Harper and Row Publishers, New York; the *Holy Bible: New International Version* (NIV). Copyright © 1973, 1978, 1984, International Bible Society. Used by permission of Zondervan Bible Publishers; J.B. Phillips: *The New Testament in Modern English, Revised Edition* (PH), © J.B. Phillips 1958, 1960, 1972, published by the Macmillan Company, New York, and Collins Publishers, London; *The Psalms for Today: A New Translation From the Hebrew Into Current English* by R.K. Harrison (HAR). Included in *Norlie's Simplified New Testament*, © 1961 by Zondervan Publishing House; *The Revised Standard Version of the Bible* (RSV), copyrighted 1946, 1952, © 1971, 1973; Richard Francis Weymouth: *The New Testament in Modern Speech*, Boston: The Pilgrim Press and London: James Clarke and Co. Ltd., 1943; Charles B. Williams: *The New Testament: A Private Translation in the Language of the People*, © 1949 The Moody Bible Institute of Chicago.

Printed in the United States of America

Contents

Authors

Warren and Ruth Myers have been on the staff of The Navigators in Singapore since 1970. Prior to their marriage in 1968, each of them had served as Navigator staff members in Asia and the United States.

Warren Myers received Jesus Christ as his personal Savior shortly before the end of World War II while serving in the U.S. Army Air Corps. Following the war he attended the University of California at Berkeley. In Berkeley he attended First Presbyterian Church, was involved in Navigator Bible study classes there, and committed himself to being available for service on the foreign mission field.

After studying religion and mechanical engineering, he graduated in 1949. That same year he attended his first Navigator conference, and was strongly impressed by the emphasis on man-to-man training and spiritual multiplication. Although previously intending to enroll in a seminary, he joined the Navigator staff in Los Angeles for three years of training and ministry.

He went to Asia for The Navigators in 1952, serving in Hong Kong, India, and Vietnam before returning to a staff position in the United States in 1960.

Ruth Myers was led by her mother to receive Christ as Savior at age 10. Following some years of spiritual doubt and questioning, she committed herself at age 16 to do whatever God might want her to do in life—including missionary work.

After high school she attended Northwestern Bible and Missionary Training School in Minneapolis, Minnesota, where she experienced new joy and vitality in her relationship with Christ. She also met Dean Denler there, who later became her husband and a Navigator staff member.

Following graduation from Bible school she attended Macalester College in Saint Paul, where she helped in the student ministry of The Navigators. She was involved in Navigator ministries in Washington, D.C. and Minneapolis before going to Taiwan in 1952 to marry Denler. She served with him in Taiwan, the Philippines, and Hong Kong before his death in 1960. She then served at The Navigators headquarters in Colorado Springs, Colorado, until her marriage with Warren.

She and Warren are both gifted Bible teachers, and have written this study from a series of Bible studies on the person of God which have been used successfully for years, primarily in Ruth's ministry.

As You Begin

God is good. He wills only the best for us. Though he is great and awesome, owning and sustaining every star and galaxy in our immense universe, he cares about us as persons. He has designed us with rich capacities for enjoyment—for tasting, seeing, feeling, thinking, loving, achieving, and worshiping—and he has "richly supplied us with all things to enjoy." With the same delicate precision he used in designing the complexities of space and the intricacies of the atom, he has formulated a plan for each of our lives, a plan that perfectly complements and develops the unique personality he envisioned before he made the world. His plan dovetails precisely with the calling and contribution he has in mind for each of us. The person and the plan were conceived together in his heart, tailor-made for each other.

In the Bible, through commands and principles, God has revealed his general plan for all people. Beyond this, his specific plan for each person includes the circumstances he permits and the individual guidance he offers. Over and over the Bible reminds us that following his plan assures our well-being and the highest fulfillment of our potential, now and forever.

Mentally we may agree that God's plan is for our greatest good. But often our struggles and reactions show that we don't truly believe it. Somewhere inside we harbor misleading ideas about God. We may feel he is a stern father who does not understand us, one intent on restricting us and cheating us of the best in life. Or we picture him as a permissive, doting grandfather; and our faith falters when his plan doesn't cater to our whims.

Often we feel we know better than God what is good for us. To some of us, "good" means being ourselves whether we are right or wrong. It means getting what we think we want, when we want it. We want what brings a present sense of pleasure, relief or achievement. God also cares about our present joy, but even more he wants to ripen our capacity for enjoyment in every aspect of our person. He wants us to learn a happiness not governed by what happens in our lives, a stable happiness that is not always threatened. He wants us to go beyond the dribbles of satisfaction we can force out of life.

Whatever misconceptions lie beneath our unbelief in God's goodness, we are losers whenever we decide to do our own thing instead of God's will. Any happiness we are able to squeeze from life by going our own way is soon marred by inner conflict. The honey we find in life gets mixed with sand. The peace we feel evaporates like dew under a scorching sun, giving way to inner disturbance or depression. The dividends we accumulate range from the second best, to the mediocre, to the intolerable.

God's plan liberates us from the emotions that rob us of joy, such as our hostilities towards others that keep us in turmoil, the distress of feeling that we never quite measure up, the fears of what people think of us, and the anxieties about our ability to cope with life. His plan brings true love into our lives—the enjoyment of his limitless, unconditional love flowing in to meet our needs and out to meet the needs of others. Into this he blends peace, gladness, and the sense of fulfillment that comes from making a significant contribution to life. "He leads out the prisoners into prosperity, only the rebellious dwell in a parched land" (Psalm 68:6 NASB).

So when God asks us to yield to him and his plan, his goal is not to limit us or deprive us of a satisfying, exciting life. When he asks us to surrender our personal plans or preferences, he offers us something better. Surrender to him never makes us less than we want to be, but always more than we can envision or achieve for ourselves. He does not destroy personality; he enhances it. He delivers us from the inner imprisonment of our imagined independence. He does this at a cost—the surrender of our autonomy. The cost is well worth paying.

"Father, use your word to make me feel deeply your love and goodness and wisdom. Correct my false ideas about you that make me shrink back from your plan for me. Give me a long-range view that believes you for the best in life today, through all the weeks and years ahead, and forever. Work in me a glad surrender of all that I am and all that I have."

> I had gone a-begging from door to door in the village path, when thy golden chariot appeared in the distance like a gorgeous dream and I wondered who was this King of all kings!
>
> My hopes rose high and me thought my evil days were at an end, and I stood waiting for alms to be given unasked and for wealth scattered on all sides in the dust.
>
> Thy chariot stopped where I stood. Thy glance fell on me and thou camest down with a smile. I felt that the luck of my life had come at last. Then of a sudden thou didst hold out thy right hand and say, "What hast thou to give to me?"
>
> Ah, what a kingly jest was it to open thy palm to a beggar to beg! I was confused and stood undecided, and then from my wallet I slowly took out the least little grain of corn and gave it to thee.
>
> But how great my surprise when at the day's end I emptied my bag on the floor to find a least little gram of gold among the poor heap. I bitterly wept and wished that I had had the heart to give thee my all.
>
> — Rabindranath Tagore
> *Gitanjali–Song Offerings*

How to Do the
Discovering God's Will Study

This Bible study and meditation series has been designed to open new and exciting avenues of biblical understanding, and to help you apply the truths you discover. Each of the topics is divided into two studies. The first, the *Experiencing God Study*, will begin to give you a rich grasp of one aspect of God's good plan; the optional *Additional Experiencing God Study* will enable you to understand the same aspect more deeply.

Approach the study prayerfully and expectantly, relying on the Holy Spirit to guide you in your desire to know God better. To further enrich your understanding, do each chapter yourself, then meet with a group which has also done it and discuss your discoveries and applications with one another.

AIDS TO YOUR STUDY

As your main Bible, use a basic version such as the *King James Version*, the *New American Standard Bible*, the *New International Version*, or the *Revised Standard Version*. You can then enrich your study by referring to one or more of the other versions and paraphrases presently available, such as *The New Testament in Modern English* by J.B. Phillips, the *Modern Language Bible* (Berkeley), the *New English Bible*, the *Good News Bible*, and *The Living Bible*.

Some questions suggest that you use a specific translation of a verse. This is indicated by an asterisk (for example, Psalm 103:5 BERK*). You will find such verses printed in full on pages 105-111.

(For additional materials which can help you in personal meditation and Bible study, and in group discussion, see *For Further Reading*, page 112.)

Begin with the *Experiencing God Study* section, and then go on to the *Additional Experiencing God Study* if you desire to pursue the topic further.

PARTS OF YOUR STUDY

Before you begin your first study, reread the *As You Begin* section of this book, marking the truths that stand out to you. Each time you do a study, you may find it profitable to review the highlights you have marked.

Begin with Prayer
As you begin to study, pray that the Holy Spirit will guide you into the truths he knows you need. Ask for both mental understanding and a life-changing experience of these truths. Look to the Lord to reveal *himself* to you in new

ways. The quotation from Rabindranath Tagore on page 6 may prove helpful as you pray.

> Pray over the Scripture, it is as the treading of grapes in the wine vat, the threshing of corn on the barn floor, the melting of gold from the ore.
> — Charles H. Spurgeon

Take Time to Meditate

Meditation, a key ingredient of this study, involves taking time to let God speak to you. Do not set out merely to answer the questions. Rather, view the questions as guides to stimulate both meditation on God's word and your personal response to God. Through prayerful meditation you can tune in to what he is saying to you and enjoy him in personal experience. So take time for each Scripture—time to look it up in two or three translations if possible, and time to absorb its meaning before you write your answer. Look for truths that will reshape your thinking, touch your emotions, and transform your attitudes and actions. Be especially alert to thoughts that help you to relate to God in a more trusting and unreserved way.

In your meditation, think about the verses phrase by phrase, using a dictionary to clarify the meaning of words you do not fully understand. Analyze what each verse is saying by emphasizing different words in the verse, by putting the verse into your own words, or by asking your own questions about it, such as:

What is the main point of this verse?
What does this Scripture reveal about God? about myself? about life?
Why is this truth important for me personally?
When and where could I use this teaching?
Is there anything in the verse that I do not understand?

As a reminder to ask yourself questions about the Scriptures, some of the questions are phrased in the first person singular (for example, "What can I learn from the following verses that will help me trust God more?")

As you meditate, mark in your Bible the things that most impress you, and jot down thoughts you may want to use later.

Answer the Questions

Write the answers to the questions in your own words; this will clarify your understanding and increase your grasp of the truths covered. When several references are given for a question, some people find it helpful to make a note of the key thoughts on scratch paper as they read the verses, and then rearrange these concepts in a brief summary.

To help your meditation, the verses are sometimes listed according to the progression of thought, rather than in the order they occur in the Bible.

Whenever appropriate, use the personal pronouns "I," "me," and "my" in answering the questions. The more personally you approach God's word, the more you open yourself to the realities it reveals.

Optional Questions

Throughout the book you will find optional questions. These can provide further valuable insights. If you are somewhat new to Bible study or if your time is limited, perhaps you should omit them, at least for now. This is especially wise if doing them would mean rushing through the other questions with too little meditation. Some people prefer to do these optional questions at a later date, when they review their study for personal profit, for leading a group discussion, or when discipling another individual.

If you are new to Bible study and yet decide to do the optional questions, do not be discouraged if you find some of them difficult. Wait to finish such questions at a later date or seek help from someone more experienced in studying the Scriptures.

Application Questions

Applying the Scriptures to daily living is a major goal of Bible study. Therefore at least one question in each study is geared specifically toward personal application of the truths you cover. Applications answer the question, "What does this aspect of God's good plan say to *me*?" Many consider this the most valuable part of the study, since it leads to closer involvement with God in everyday life and can become a stepping-stone to greater enjoyment, obedience, and fruitfulness.

Pray for the Holy Spirit to apply the word to your life, guiding you to the response he has in mind. Sometimes he indicates specific, practical applications dealing with our relationships or activities. At other times he leads us to praise God for some truth about himself or to pray regarding a needy area of our life. Sometimes he gives us a change of viewpoint; or he wants us to expose ourselves again and again to a truth, while counting on him to produce an ever-increasing inner transformation as we do so. However, if you find yourself *consistently* choosing for your applications either outward steps or inner responses to the exclusion of the other, seek to strike a balance. God uses the Scriptures to mold both what we think and how we act.

The essential element in application is that you not merely examine the Scriptures but also let them examine you. You can pray, "Lord, I come to you and to your word as my sovereign authority. I do not come to *make* it speak to me or wrench from it a satisfactory application, but to *let* you speak to my heart and work in my life as you choose." Then be as specific in what you write as he leads you to be.

An application may be drawn from one phrase, one verse, or the whole study. State clearly your need, how this passage meets it, and what God is leading you to do.

Here are a few examples of possible steps to take:
- Memorize the verse that especially speaks to you and review it daily with praise and prayer.
- Say "yes" to God on some specific issue.
- Say "no" to some activity or relationship that hinders your spiritual growth.
- Go to a friend or loved one, confess an offense and ask forgiveness.
- Ask a friend or spiritual leader to pray for you in the specific need involved.
- Begin your quiet time each day for a week with prayer about the matter that concerns you.
- Decide to begin some new habit in experiencing God and his good plan, such as a regular quiet time, consistent Scripture memory, or a monthly half-day of prayer.
- Plan to meditate on your *Brief Statement of Truth* several times a day and consciously use it whenever you have a need.

Brief Statement of Truth

In some of the topics you are asked to write a brief statement of some truth that stands out to you. This can prove valuable for on-the-spot use in applying the truth to specific personal needs. It helps you get a grip on the truth in a usable way so that it can rescue you when contrary thoughts, feelings, desires, or distractions hinder your response to God. Decide first which passage or thought in your study most powerfully moves you. Find one that challenges you to action, or causes you to want a closer relationship with God, or corrects a misconception about him, or helps you respond to him more obediently.

a. Copy the verse or part of it:

> "I will rejoice over doing them good, and I will plant them... with all my heart and with all my soul."
> Jeremiah 32:41, BERK

b. Rewrite the verse in personalized form, using personal pronouns:

> God will rejoice over doing me good, and he will plant me with all his heart and with all his soul.

c. Make your own concise statement on the verse or thought:

> God works for my good with wholehearted delight; he is never grudging or disinterested in helping me.

d. Choose a quote from someone else that touches your heart:

> "I'll strengthen thee, help thee, and cause thee to stand, Upheld by my gracious, omnipotent hand."
> —from the song, "How Firm a Foundation"

The object is to have one concise statement that moves you deeply in a constructive way—one that meets a specific need or motivates you to trust or appreciate God and his plan for you. Since it is brief, you can easily memorize it and meditate on it frequently.

Sometimes you will quickly find your *Brief Statement of Truth* because a passage captures your attention or meets an obvious need. At other times you may have to pray earnestly for truths that will help you in specific ways.

Perhaps you are frequently troubled by distressing emotions (such as resentment, anger, envy, anxiety, fear, self-condemnation, or depression); or by disruptive outer responses to other people (such as angry outbursts, withdrawal, impatience, negativism, or a critical spirit). Behind these obvious negative areas in your life you can often find false beliefs that trigger them. For example, you may consciously believe that God is reliable, but frequent anxieties may point to a hidden belief that he will fail you. Or beneath your self-condemnation may be the hidden belief that Christ's sacrifice is not enough to assure total forgiveness, but that you must add an appropriate degree of self-punishment in order to deserve his blessing. Behind depression may be the belief that you are worthless, or that you have no significant reason to live.

Seek to become aware of any hidden false beliefs that underlie your feelings and reactions, and find truths that will serve as antidotes to them. Pray frequently about this: "Lord, show me any false convictions that cause my negative emotions and reactions, and lead me to the scriptural truths that I can use again and again to counteract these false ideas and to produce in me positive emotions and responses to people."

Then be alert as you do these studies to find the *Brief Statements of Truth* that you most need—statements through which God can further transform your thoughts and liberate you. When he gives you an appropriate statement, prayerfully go over it in your times alone with him. Meditate on it until it grips your heart and stirs your imagination. Feed it into the depths of your mind frequently and with conviction.

Later, in your times of conscious need or failure, do three things. First, *acknowledge* what is happening in your thoughts, feelings, or reactions. Second, *choose against* being overwhelmed or led astray. Third, consciously and emphatically *think* on your brief statement, thanking God that it is true. Keep meditating on it until the temptation passes or the need is met.

Finding and using *Brief Statements of Truth* can be a key to increased liberation in your life, for Jesus promises, "you shall know the truth, and the truth shall make you free" (John 8:32).

Favorite Passages (for future meditation and praise)
The goal of this study is to think about God's word in a life-transforming way, both as you initially do the study and in the future. To promote future

meditation, be alert to note the verses in each chapter that especially stand out to you. Reexamine such verses, and choose the statements or phrases that most help you to understand and feel the reality of the truth you are studying. Copy these in the *Favorite Passages* section.

Aim to record a few truths that particularly impress you rather than copying many passages. After you tune in your heart to each aspect of God and his good plan, you will be more alert to finding additional Scriptures as you have your quiet time, listen to messages, and discuss the word with your friends. By adding new verses when they impress you, you can expand your study in the coming days, months, and even years. Insert additional blank pages if you need them.

Take time to appreciate and worship God in connection with the truths you are discovering. Appreciation and worship are vitally important—they uplift your own spirit and bring pleasure and glory to God. Cultivate the habit of turning often to the *Favorite Passages* part of your studies for further reflection and praise. You can do this at the beginning of your quiet time, in family devotions, or before going to bed. Return to these parts also when you need fresh motivation in experiencing God's goodness and trusting his plan for your life.

In some chapters, you will be asked to examine specific passages and to copy the ones that impress you. Study such verses in the sequence listed, looking them up in two or three translations if possible and meditating carefully on each one. Then copy the verses or parts of verses that mean most to you.

For the topic, "I Can Trust God's Plan," your *Favorite Passages* part might look like this:

Favorite Passages

"... Who satisfies you throughout life with good things."
Psalm 103:4 BERK

"No good thing does He withold from those who walk uprightly."
Psalm 84:11 NASB

"How well he understands us and knows what is best for us at all times."
Ephesians 1:8 LB

"O Lord, thou art my God; I will exalt thee, I will praise thy name; for thou hast done wonderful things, plans formed of old, faithful and sure."
Isaiah 25:1 RSV

Notes and Quotes
As you do your study, record here any other special thoughts that relate to the subject. Both as you are studying and in the coming months, try to collect quotations, poems, and illustrations that will enrich your appreciation of the

topic. For illustrations, be alert to things learned from Jesus, other Bible personalities, outstanding Christians of the past and present, Christian friends, and your own experiences.

Ideas for extra study
If you have time for further study and meditation, look over the ideas below. These extras will both enhance your personal study and help prepare you to use the study with individuals or groups. If you do not have time for them now, you may want to do them later when preparing to use the study with others.

a. Write a *Brief Statement of Truth* for each lesson.
b. Plan how to share some aspect of the truth you are studying with another person. Many times you can first share how you need this truth and how you want it to affect *your* life. Then the two of you can pray together about each other's needs.
c. Plan a talk on the subject. See *Chapter 12*, page 94, for ideas.
d. Look for other verses that relate to the topic, copying them in your *Favorite Passages* section or adding them as cross references to various questions. You can find them from verses memorized, cross-references in your Bible, or a concordance.
e. Jot down any problems you have in understanding the verses or truths. See if another translation throws light on your problem, or try asking someone who is more mature spiritually. A book of word studies can sometimes prove helpful, or a good commentary, especially if you use it *after* your personal and original investigation of the Scriptures.
f. Make a special attempt to find illustrations, quotations, or poems that enrich your appreciation of the subject being studied. Spend some time searching for illustrations from the historical narratives in the Bible.
g. Meet with someone else to pray about your understanding and application of the truths covered.

Reviewing your study
Be alert to times of pressure or need when your heart can be refreshed and your faith strengthened by reviewing your study. It is important that we get a grip on truth *and* that truth gets a grip on us. This will increasingly happen as you review and pray about your study again and again.

> You may look lightly upon the Scripture and see nothing; meditate often upon it and there you shall see a light like the light of the sun.
> —Joseph Caryl (1647)
> *The Shadow of the Broad Brim*

1. I Can Trust God's Plan

As you meditate on the Scriptures in this study, take special note of the verses or phrases that most strongly encourage you to trust God and his plan for you. Copy these from your Bible into the *Favorite Passages* section on page 18. In the future, add other verses that speak to you in a definite way about this topic. Use your *Favorite Passages* section often for meditation and praise.

1. Before you begin to study, pray that in new ways you will see how qualified God is to plan your life and how trustworthy his plans are.

    The Lord alone can prepare the mind to receive the Scriptures. —Charles H. Spurgeon

2. What can I be sure of if I let God lead me? Psalm 23:6; Psalm 103:5 BERK*.

3. What is God's attitude toward us and how did he show it? 1 John 4:9-10; Romans 8:32.

    In view of God's attitude, why can we safely trust his plan for us?

4. Meditate on the following verses and write a short paragraph about the results of trusting God and submitting to his plan. Psalm 34:8-10; Isaiah 48:17-18 NIV*; Deuteronomy 5:29.

5. Psalm 84:11 compares God to two things. What are they and what are their functions?

Objects	Functions

* All verses from other translations are supplied on pages 104-109.

Further observations about Psalm 84:11 that increase your sense of his goodness:

6. God intends not to deprive us but to delight us. As I choose him above the enticing-but-passing pleasures of sin, he reshapes my values and desires, and provides for their fulfillment. What does he provide?

What God provides	Further impressions
Psalm 19:8-10 Jeremiah 15:16	
Psalm 36:8-9	
Psalm 94:19 NASB*	
Job 22:23-26	

"God is the answer to our deepest longings" (1 Corinthians 6:13 paraphrased).

7. Read Philippians 3:4-8. If I seek Christ first as Paul did and begin to experience the surpassing value of knowing him better, what will fade into insignificance by comparison?

What things in my life need to lose importance so that I may know and experience Christ more fully?

8. Which of the *Favorite Passages* you have recorded most encourages you to trust God's plan for you? (Reference and key thought).

1. I Can Trust God's Plan (continued)

1. The following Scriptures further show how God is qualified to plan our lives. In your *Favorite Passages* section copy from the following verses the statements that mean the most to you regarding God's intentions and attitudes toward you. Psalm 100:5; Jeremiah 32:40-41 BERK*; 2 Corinthians 8:9; Ephesians 1:8 LB*; 1 John 4:18 LB*.

2. What do the following passages reveal about the Lord's plans for his people? Psalm 40:5; Isaiah 25:1; Ephesians 1:9.

3. If I trust the Lord and center my hopes in him, what will be true of my life and effectiveness? Jeremiah 17:7-8.

   What do you think heat and drought in a person's life refer to?

4. The Chaldeans (Babylonians) were besieging Jerusalem (Zion) and the city greatly feared being captured by them. At that point God sent them a hard-to-believe message. According to Jeremiah 38:2, 17-20, what was God's plan for his people at that point?

   To envision how this plan looked from the human viewpoint, imagine yourself protected in a walled city besieged by a fierce, violent, dreaded enemy, and being asked to go out and surrender yourself to that enemy, having only God's revealed will and promises to encourage you. Then look up the following passages (in which "Israel," "Jacob" and "Judah" all refer to the Jewish people)—Jeremiah 24:4-7, 29:10, 31:1-4, 10-14, 17. These verses describe the blessings and restoration that God promised to those who would follow his plan. Briefly describe what God promised to do and copy the statements that most appeal to you and give you a sense of God's goodness.

History later proved these promises to be true. Those taken captive (605 and 586 B.C.) were able to build houses, plant gardens, eat of the produce, and multiply in number. Then in about 536 B.C. after Cyrus king of Persia had captured Babylon, he made a proclamation that provided both freedom and finances for the people to return to their homeland.

Optional:

Read Psalm 1. What makes a person blessed or happy?

How is the non-blessed person described?

What insights and feelings do you get from the illustrations (both positive and negative) in this Psalm?

5. As we open ourselves to God, his blessing in our lives can link us with a broader purpose than just our own well-being. What is that exciting purpose? Psalm 67:1-2, 7.

6. Write a short paragraph summarizing what you have learned about why you can trust God's plan for you.

7. What thoughts, feelings, attitudes or reservations tend to hinder you from submitting to God's plan, either in the basic decision to let him be your Lord or in smaller decisions?

8. To increase your trust in God's plan for you, write a *Brief Statement of Truth* about something from this study that impresses you. Use it frequently. (See instructions, pages 10-11).

Favorite Passages

Notes and Quotes. *Add your own as you discover them.*

Sample:

All the good things that can be reckoned up here below have only a finite and limited goodness. Some can clothe but cannot feed; others can nourish but cannot secure; others adorn but cannot advance; all do serve but none do satisfy. They are like a beggar's coat made up of many pieces, not all enough either to beautify or defend. But Christ is full and sufficient for all His people . . . He is bread, wine, milk, living waters, to feed them; He is a garment of righteousness to cover and adorn them; a Physician to heal them; a Counsellor to advise them; a Captain to defend them; a Prince to rule; a Prophet to teach; a Priest to make atonement for them; a Husband to protect; a Father to provide; a Brother to relieve, a Foundation to support; a Root to quicken; a Head to guide; a Treasure to enrich; a Sun to enlighten; and a Fountain to cleanse; so that as the one ocean hath more waters than all the rivers of the world; and one sun provides more light than all the luminaries in heaven, so one Christ is more to a poor soul than if it had all the world a thousand times over.

—John Spencer

2. I Cannot Trust My Own Plans

As you study this topic, copy in your *Favorite Passages* section on page 24 the verses or phrases of Scripture that most make you distrust your own plans.

1. Pray to see more clearly your human limitations and the foolishness of choosing your own plans rather than God's.

    A prayerless Christian will never learn God's truth. —E.M. Bounds

2. A true look at ourselves compared to God can change us; it can help dissolve the independent self-confidence or fear that urges us to insist on our own plans. Look up the following verses and record below the contrasts you discover. Romans 11:33; Job 9:4; James 4:13-16; Proverbs 28:26; Ecclesiastes 11:9.

Why God's way is best	Why trusting my way is foolish

3. According to the following verses, why can we not trust our own wisdom? Jeremiah 10:23; Proverbs 14:12.

4. The following verses further describe the results of going one's own way, and living independently of God. Matthew 7:26-27; Psalm 106:13-15; Ecclesiastes 2:11, and 2:22-23; Deuteronomy 28:65-67 BERK*.

    a. List the various results of such independence, underlining the ones you consider most serious.

* The verses from other translations are printed on pages 104-109.

b. What do you think are some root reasons why people live this way?

5. Many of Jeremiah's prophecies were written largely to people who consistently disregarded God's commands, resisting his plan in spite of repeated warnings and chastenings (Jeremiah 5:3, 23-25). What did these people ask about the suffering they experienced? What was God's reply? Jeremiah 13:22, and 16:10-12.

Sometimes we want to plan our own lives because we fear that God's plans will mean suffering or unhappiness. We forget that every life includes suffering. If we go our own way, we face life's troubles and bereavements without God's help and comfort—and our willfulness brings us chastening that we could have avoided.

> *A man by his sin can waste himself, which is to waste that on earth which is most like God. This is man's greatest tragedy, God's greatest grief.*
>
> —A.W. Tozer

Optional:
When we resist God's plan, what are we saying about ourselves in comparison to God? What basic sin does this involve? James 4:6.

Can you think of other Scriptures that warn against this sin and its results?

6. Review the questions in this study and write a brief warning for yourself, pinpointing your greatest need in these areas.

God wants us to acknowledge our limitations and believe that he is qualified to direct our lives. Then our handicaps become assets that contribute to a glad trust in his plan. The songwriter discovered this:

> *God holds the key of all unknown,*
> > *And I am glad:*
> *If other hands should hold the key,*
> *Or if He trusted it to me,*
> > *I might be sad.*
>
> *The very dimness of my sight*
> > *Makes me secure;*
> *For, groping in my misty way,*
> *I feel His hand; I hear Him say,*
> > *"My help is sure."*
> > > —Author unknown.

2. I Cannot Trust My Own Plans (continued)

1. Consider Jeremiah 17:5-6 BERK*.
   a. Why is the person described in these verses under God's disfavor?

   b. A juniper tree or heath in the desert is a stunted, dry, unattractive bush whose leaves are often eaten away by wild goats. What do you think is implied by "parched places" and "uninhabited salt land" as they apply to a person's situations in life?

2. In the book of Jeremiah, we learn how God's people persistently resisted his plans for them. Consider the following verses: Jeremiah 2:13, 30-32; 6:10, 16-19; 18:11-12.
   a. What were their wrong attitudes and responses to God?

   b. What did God say would be the result? Jeremiah 18:11.

Optional:
Man's idea of running his own life to get what he wanted began in Genesis 3:1-6. What were Satan's words as he tried to convince Eve:
   a. That God's warning about the results of sin wasn't true?

   b. That God was withholding something good from her and that her life would be better if she went her own way in spite of God's warning?

What consequences did Adam and Eve suffer as a result of their selfish decision? Eve, Genesis 3:16; Adam, 3:17-19; both 3:7-10, 22-24.

A modern version of Satan's lies: "Come with us and you will get your eyes opened. You can be like God—utterly free, able to do your own thing. Besides, it is psychologically unhealthy and inhibiting to be good, and everyone knows that authority and absolutes are outdated. Nothing is wrong if it is meaningful to you and does not hurt anybody. You have to break the rules and experiment. That is where the excitement is."

3. From Colossians 2:8 and 2 Timothy 3:1-8, jot down several ways that modern people express their independence of God.

4. Whether it leads to unconventional living or being a respectable, dependable citizen and neighbor, running one's life independently of God is senseless and fatal. How does God describe this in Ephesians 4:17-18 PH?*

5. Instead of the freedom, satisfaction, and self-realization that Satan promises, what are the results when we go our own way instead of God's? John 8:34; Proverbs 5:12-13; Revelation 3:17; Galatians 6:7-8 PH*; Titus 3:3.

Make me a captive, Lord,
  And then I shall be free;
Force me to render up my sword
  And I shall conqueror be.
I sink in life's alarm
  When in myself I stand;
Imprison with Thy mighty arm,
  Then strong shall be my hand.

My will is not my own
  Till Thou hast made it Thine;
If it would reach a monarch's throne
  It must its crown resign:
  It only stands unbent
  Amid the clashing strife,
When on Thy bosom it has leant
  And found in Thee its life.
      —George Matheson

To be enslaved to oneself is the heaviest of all servitudes. —Seneca, about 60 A.D.

6. In what areas of your life are you most likely to resist God's plan and trust your own?

Which verses in this study most challenge you to go God's way instead of your own?

Optional:
In this study what two or three things about God most impress you?

If God be thy portion, there is no condition that can make thee miserable: if God be not thy portion, in the midst of thy sufficiency thou wilt be in straits. O sirs, it is not absolutely necessary that you should have this or that earthly portion, but it is absolutely necessary that you should have God.

—Thomas Brooks

Favorite Passages

Notes and Quotes. *Add your own as you discover them.*

Sample:
With thoughtless and
  Impatient hands
    We tangle up
    The plans
The Lord hath wrought.

And when we cry
  In pain, He saith,
  "Be quiet, dear,
While I untie the knot."
        —V. Raymond Edman
            The Disciplines of Life

3. God Can Fulfill His Plans

God wants what is best for us. He also knows what is best, and he has the power to bring his good plan to fulfillment. He is sovereign over the entire universe, the supreme ruler of all creation. He is "limited" only by his wisdom and purposes, by his own character, and by choices he himself has made—never by the power of nature or created beings, never by the circumstances of our lives.

Yet in blessing and guiding us as individuals, God has chosen to let us limit him by our spiritual and moral choices. He fulfills his good intentions for each of us if we *let* him do so, if we submit to his sovereignty and trust him.

1. Pray you will know God's sovereign control in a more life-changing way. Consider praying this as you awake each morning while you are studying this topic.

    There is only one limit to what prayer can do; that is what God can do. —R.A. Torrey

2. From the passages below, copy in the *Favorite Passages* section the verses or phrases that most impress you about God's ability to fulfill his plans and purposes. Add other verses as you discover them. (If you studied *Experiencing God's Attributes*, you may want to review chapter four, God's Ability and Power, and chapter nine, God's Sovereignty.)

    1 Chronicles 29:11-13; Psalm 115:3; Isaiah 43:13, and 46:9-10; Daniel 2:20-21 LB*.

3. Summarize what Psalm 33:10-11; Isaiah 14:24, 27; and Acts 5:38-39 say about trying to oppose God's counsel or plans.

4. What can I count on even when I fear that my life will be adversely affected by someone's mistakes, or even evil intentions? Genesis 50:20; Psalm 31:19-20; Revelation 3:7-8.

5. What does God say about the seemingly chance happenings in my life? Proverbs 16:33 AMP*; 1 Peter 1:7 PH*.

Note: Remember that using another translation of the Bible often throws new light on the verses you study.

Optional:
In Isaiah 44:24-45:7 (written about 700 B.C.) and in Jeremiah 25:11-12 and 29:10 (written about 100 years later), what did the Lord specifically predict about the captivity and restoration of Judah and Jerusalem?

Summarize what happened in 2 Chronicles 36:22-23 and Ezra 1:1-8 (events that occurred in 536 B.C., nearly two centuries after Isaiah wrote).

What statements in these chapters especially emphasize the truth that God is able to fulfill his purposes and plans?

God knows the future and personally shapes the history of his people, both individually and collectively.

He has the film of my whole life in view, and not just the snapshot of my present situation.
—Walter Trobisch

There is a simplicity about God in working out His plans, yet a resourcefulness equal to any difficulty, and an unswerving faithfulness to His trusting child, and an unforgetting steadiness in holding to His purpose. . . .It is safe to trust God's methods and to go by His clock.
—S.D. Gordon

6.Review this study and list some major truths you have discovered about God's sovereign control.

7. Select one of the truths you have learned and tell how it relates to your life or attitudes.

God never plans that people should sin, but he always has a plan to take care of the sin and to handle every situation. God's plan and his ideal will are not always synonymous; perhaps in a fallen world they are rarely the same. He permits many things to happen that are contrary to his will; but before time began, he incorporated them into his plan, to bring about his long-range purposes for the world and, most of all, for every human who willingly submits to him.

Note: As you study the topics in this book, jot down any questions you have about the verses and their applications. See if another translation throws light on your problem, or try asking someone who is more mature spiritually.

3. God Can Fulfill His Plans (continued)

God's sovereign working aims not only to fulfill his plan for our personal lives but also to reach out through us to meet the needs of others. Through believing prayer and action, we can be conduits of his power and blessings. By unbelief we become obstructions, both in our own lives and other people's. The more we are convinced of his position, power, and wisdom, the more we will trust him and free his mighty hand to work.

1. How would you describe the Lord's power and authority? Ephesians 1:19-21 PH*; 1 Timothy 6:15; Ecclesiastes 3:14.

2. From Jeremiah 32:17 and 27, what do you learn about the extent of God's influence and involvement and the greatness of his power?

3. In God's plan for his own people and for world history, what is often true of his timing compared to ours? Why? 2 Peter 3:8-9; Isaiah 30:18 RSV*.

4. When his timing seems slow, what does God ask of us, and why? Lamentations 3:25-26; Hebrews 10:36; Psalm 37:7.

Sometimes when I seem to be waiting for God, he is waiting for me. Does he delay answering my prayers for changes in my situation or in another person? Perhaps he must first accomplish his purposes in me. Perhaps he is waiting for me to pray, "Lord, how do you want to change *me* before you grant this external blessing or deliverance?"

5. What is God often waiting for his people to do? Lamentations 3:40-41; 2 Chronicles 7:14.

6. From the Bible or elsewhere, can you think of some examples of God's delays and how he demonstrated that they were part of his plan for good?

God's plan includes both "what" and "when." As we prayerfully trust God and keep his commandments, he keeps us synchronized with his perfect timetable.

> *He that believeth shall not make haste*
> *In useless hurry his strength to waste.*
> *Who walks with God can afford to wait,*
> *For He can never arrive too late.*
>
> *He that believeth shall not delay;*
> *Who carries the Word of the King on its way*
> *Keeps pace with the Pleiades' marching tune,*
> *And he can never arrive too soon.*
>
> *He that believeth shall walk serene,*
> *With ordered steps and leisured mien.*
> *He dwells in the midst of eternities,*
> *And the timeless ages of God are his.*
> —Annie Johnson Flint

7. 2 Chronicles 20 vividly illustrates God's sovereign ability to fulfill his purposes for the good of his people. Read verses 1-30 and record what you discover about:

The predicament

The preparation

The battle

The benefits

What statement in 2 Chronicles 20 most affects your heart response to God's sovereignty in relation to your own life?

He has the power to work even in the feeblest of His servants with the strength of the almighty God. He has power even to use their apparent impotence to carry out His purposes. He has the power over every enemy and every human heart, over every difficulty and danger.

—Andrew Murray

Optional:

Many of the "all things" in Scripture emphasize God's ability to fulfill his plans and purposes:

He works all things after the counsel of His own will.	Ephesians 1:11
He upholds all things by the word of His power.	Hebrews 1:3
He is able to subject all things to Himself.	Philippians 3:20-21
All things are His servants.	Psalm 119:91

Can you add any other "all things" to the above list?

8. Review what you have studied in this chapter, and write one reference and a brief statement of its truth for each question below.

   a. What most comforts and encourages me?

   b. What challenges me to submit to God and his plan for me?

Favorite Passages

Notes and Quotes. *Add your own as you discover them.*

Sample:
He writes in characters too grand
For our short sight to understand;
We catch but broken strokes, and try
To fathom all the mystery
Of withered hopes, of death, of life,
The endless war, the useless strife—
But there, with larger, clearer sight,
We shall see this—His way was right.
                              —John Oxenham

4. Why God Includes Trials

As you meditate on the Scriptures in this study, copy under *Favorite Passages* (page 38) the Bible verses or phrases that most impress you as to the place trials have in God's plan for your good.

1. Pray you will know God better and more clearly understand his purposes in trials, "so that you may be able to pass through any experience and endure it with joy" (Colossians 1:11 PH).

    Prayer is the slender nerve that moves the mighty hand of God.

2. What do you learn about trials from the following verses:

Passage	What trials can do for us	What our responses should be
James 1:2-5 PH*		
Romans 5:2-5 LB*		
Hebrews 12:3-10		
Job 12:10-12		
Psalm 119:50 119:67 119:71		

Comments

"I know, O Lord, that thy judgments are right, and that in faithfulness thou hast afflicted me" (Psalm 119:75 RSV).

> *The chief pang of most trials is not so much the suffering itself as our own spirit of resistance to it.*
>
> —Jean Nicholas Grou

3. What truths do you see in 2 Corinthians 1:3-5 that help you understand why God permits sufferings, trials, and pressures?

4. What could happen if the Lord allowed only blessings in our lives? Hosea 13:6.

5. If I love the Lord, what can I be sure of even in difficulties or disappointments? Romans 8:28.

   What is included in the "good" toward which all things work? Romans 8:29 LB*.

Optional:

Can you think of scriptural accounts showing good things God has done for his people through trials?

Reference	Brief description of the trial and its good results

Illustration—Romans 8:28-29

When we bake a cake we have a picture in mind of the delicious, beautiful end product we want to produce. For each type of cake we have a recipe that includes the exact ingredients needed, the amount of mixing required, the heat of the oven, and the length of time it should be baked.

   The Lord has in mind a beautiful end product for our life: our unique personality set free and radiating the beauty of his Son. And for each of us he has a special "recipe." Sometimes we argue with him. "But, Lord, you did not put that much oil in for John—and for Susie, you put in more chocolate. And please, not that much sugar—two cups of plain sugar! Could we omit that awful cream of tartar? Oh, no—I just cannot stand a dozen egg whites. By the way, Lord, I have decided to be strawberry, not angel food. Stop! You have beaten long enough. George's recipe only calls for one minute of heavy beating—it's not fair if mine is two minutes. And 30 minutes in the oven at 375 degrees! Please, Lord, turn down the heat!"

"But dear, the cake will not taste as good—it will be lumpy or soggy or half baked. Just trust me, and we will both be delighted with the results! 'I know the plans I have for you, plans for welfare and not for evil, to give you a future and a hope'" (Jeremiah 29:11).

With God nothing is incidental, nothing is accidental, and no experience is wasted.

6. As we become aware of emotional and spiritual thirsts through trials, what can we do? Psalm 63:1, John 7:37-38.

Can Jesus meet my need? Yes, and more than meet it. No matter how intricate my path, how difficult my service; no matter how sad my bereavement, how far away my loved ones; no matter how helpless I am, how deep are my soul-yearnings —Jesus can meet all, all and more than meet!

—Hudson Taylor

7. What is the most difficult thing you are facing? Describe it briefly.

From the Scriptures you have considered in this study select two truths you can thank God for, and two things you want to ask him to do in your life. For a week or so, use these daily for thanksgiving and prayer.
Reasons for thanksgiving:
a.

b.

Things for God to accomplish in me:
a.

b.

8. Which of the Scriptures in this study helps you the most, and in what way?

Optional:
Do one or two of the extras suggested on page 13.

4. Why God Includes Trials (continued)

1. Look up the following verses, meditate on them, and add the most meaningful portions to your *Favorite Passages* section. Deuteronomy 8:2-3; Psalm 94:12-13 BERK*; Luke 22:31-32; John 16:33; 1 Peter 1:6-7.

2. From the above verses, list some reasons why God allows trials in our lives.

3. What do you learn from Job 1:12; 2:6, and 1 Corinthians 10:13 about trials and testings and who controls their limits?

4. Sometimes God tests us through great trials—sometimes through "the tiny pin-prick troubles that annoy, the squeaking wheels that grate upon our joy." Below are some important considerations about attitudes in facing trials, large or small.

Exodus 17:2; 16:8; Psalm 37:1, 8; Philippians 2:14-15.

Wrong attitudes and reactions	Why we should avoid these

Causes of harmful attitudes and reactions—Psalm 78:8, 32, and 106:25.

How to prevent and overcome negative reactions, despondency, or despair
Psalm 78:7-8, and 119:92-93; Hebrews 12:2-3 BERK*.

5. What attitude is especially dangerous? Why? Hebrews 12:15.

6. How did Jesus feel about the crushing trial that came upon him in Gethsemane? Yet what attitude did he choose? Matthew 26:36-42.

7. God asks us to accept our trials, welcoming them as friends. The opposite response is an inner resistance or stiffening of heart. When my peace is disturbed, I should ask, "What am I resisting, Lord?" Check or underline the things that most easily trigger negative reactions in you:

— changes the Lord wants to make in me or my life patterns
— disappointments that don't let me have my way
— interruptions that keep me from accomplishing my goals
— the grace and sufficiency of the Lord, choosing instead my own self-dependence and desire for personal credit and glory
— evidence of my own need, guilt, inadequacy, or failure
— the Lord's solution to my problem when it differs from my own
— the people who I feel have wronged me
— the Lord's desire to control my life
— an authority God has placed over me (parent, husband, employer, government, spiritual leader)
— sickness or another physical affliction

These resistings stem from wanting to protect myself from anything that undercuts my natural preferences and feelings of being approved. They show that I am not trusting the Lord to protect me and meet my needs. A wholehearted acceptance of what God permits or sends opens us to his grace for making positive adjustments, and tunes us in to his wisdom for possible constructive responses and actions.

The Lord may not have definitely planned that this should overtake me, but He has most certainly permitted it. Therefore, though it were an attack of an enemy, by the time it reaches me, it has the Lord's permission, and all is well. He will make it work together with all of life's experiences for good.

—C.W. Welch

8. Thanking and praising God, whether or not we feel like it, can repeatedly liberate us from negative attitudes. Consider 1 Thessalonians 5:18, Ephesians 5:20, and Hebrews 13:15. Try this on one area of need you have discovered in doing this study.

Only during my brief stay on earth can I give God the pleasure of praising him in the midst of pain.

—Dean Denler, while hospitalized with terminal cancer.

9. Prayerfully review the questions and your answers above, asking the Lord to clarify any attitudes that are harmful or that limit you. In what situations and relationships do they occur and what steps can you take to overcome them?

George Müller's faith when facing trials is vividly shown in his response to a problem-filled situation in 1843.

"I had a secret satisfaction in the greatness of the difficulties which were in the way. So far from being cast down on account of them, they delighted my soul; for I only desired to do the will of the Lord in this matter . . . the greater the obstacles, the more abundantly plain the proof that I had come to a right judgment if they were removed by prayer . . . I did nothing but pray. Prayer and faith, the universal remedies against every want and every difficulty, and the nourishment of prayer and faith, God's holy Word, helped me over all the difficulties."

—George Müller
quoted by Roger Steer in *George Müller: Delighted in God*

Favorite Passages

Notes and Quotes. *Add your own as you discover them.*

Samples:
"God gets His best soldiers out of
The highlands of affliction."

"Sorrows come to stretch out spaces
in the heart for joy."

I will not doubt, though all my ships at sea
  Come drifting home with broken masts and sails;
  I will believe the Hand which never fails,
  From seeming evil worketh good for me.
And though I weep because those sails are tattered,
  Still will I cry, while my best hopes lie shattered:
    "I trust in Thee."
                                   —Ella Wheeler Wilcox

5. God's Plan and Who I Am

As you meditate on the Scriptures in this study, be alert to those that give you a clearer sense of who you are. In your *Favorite Passages* section, copy the ones you like best. Review them often, with praise.

1. Pray to know God better and to see yourself from his viewpoint.

> *"And I pray that your participation in the faith may result in action as you come to a fuller realization of the wealth of good things in you through your union with Christ Jesus."*
>
> —Philemon 6 (from several translations).

2. Consider Psalm 139:13-14 LB* and Psalm 119:73.

   a. What do you learn about God and yourself?

   Psalm 139:15 in various translations says that I was "skillfully wrought," "intricately fashioned," or "embroidered with great skill."

   b. Because God designed and formed you, how should you evaluate yourself? What should your response to him be?

3. What do the following verses teach about each person who has been born again into God's family through personal faith in Jesus Christ?

References	Facts about me as God's child
John 5:24	
Romans 5:1	
Ephesians 1:7	
Colossians 1:13	
1 John 3:1	

References	Facts about me as God's child
Romans 8:15-17	
Ephesians 1:3	
Ephesians 1:11 LB*	
Philippians 4:13	

Which one or two truths from your answers above most encourage and assure you?

4. How do 2 Corinthians 5:17 and Ephesians 2:10 describe who we are "in Christ"?

   "His workmanship" could be translated "his design" or "his poem." Each of us, both naturally as his creation and spiritually as his new creation, is a work of art, a product of God's creativity, one of his "originals."

5. You have been meditating on a few of the uplifting truths the Bible gives about yourself. To enjoy these truths fully, you must also accept the humbling facts God reveals. From the following verses describe the negative and needy sides of who you are.
   a. Romans 3:23, and 7:18.

   b. 2 Corinthians 3:5; John 15:5.

   For a healthy, realistic view of ourselves, we must admit the negatives. Then we must go on to focus with thanksgiving on the positives—the wonderful truths about how unique and valuable, how forgiven and accepted, how adequate we are to face life through Christ.

   To believe, and to consent to be loved while unworthy, is the great secret.
   —William R. Newell

6. Review Questions 2-5 and record below the verses or phrases that most make you feel thankful and self-accepting.

7. Do you find it hard to believe any of the above truths or to enjoy their reality? Which ones, and why do you think you feel this way?

8. In your quiet time this week, use Question 6 for thanksgiving and Question 7 for prayer. Ask God to implant these truths deep in your thoughts and feelings, and to melt away any barriers to accepting them.

> *The meek man is not a human mouse afflicted with a sense of his own inferiority. Rather he may be in his moral life as bold as a lion and as strong as Samson; but he has stopped being fooled about himself.*
>
> *He has accepted God's estimate of his own life. He knows he is as weak and helpless as God has declared him to be, but paradoxically, he knows at the same time that in the sight of God he is of more importance than angels. In himself, nothing; in God, everything. That is his motto.*
>
> *He knows well that the world will never see him as God sees him and he has stopped caring. He rests perfectly content to allow God to place His own values. He will be patient to wait for the day when everything will get its own price tag and real worth will come into its own. Then the righteous shall shine forth in the Kingdom of their Father.*
>
> —A.W. Tozer,
> *The Pursuit of God*

5. God's Plan and Who I Am (continued)

Does God do a good job in designing some people and a poor job in designing others? Does he sometimes make inferior or worthless products unsuited for the purposes he has in mind? Does his hand slip at times, marring his work; or did he merely "let us happen" and later try to make the most of the result? The Scriptures give exciting insights into these questions, insights that both humble and uplift us.

1. Jot down below any personal questions on this subject that trouble you. Begin praying for satisfactory answers, and for grace to trust God's goodness and wisdom in things you do not yet understand.

2. God is grieved if I resent what I am like—*or* if I take credit for any of my characteristics or abilities. Why is self-congratulation unwarranted? John 3:27; 1 Corinthians 4:7.

   Humility does not mean denying my admirable qualities, but acknowledging them with gratefulness, giving God the credit for them. It means honoring other people also as God's handiwork, created in his image. As the author of our lives, he has given each of us the basic personality and abilities that best fit the purposes and position he has in mind for us. Humility honors God by accepting his workmanship.

3. If I do not accept myself (including my physical characteristics, my inherent personality, my natural abilities, and my spiritual gifts), a) how am I relating to God; and b) what am I implying about him? Romans 9:20; Isaiah 29:16 RSV*.

   If I feel superior to other people, disregard their good qualities, and magnify myself, what am I saying about God as our creator?

4. My natural reaction is to resent and hide the ways I fall short of the ideal person I would prefer to be. Instead, what attitude should I take toward my weaknesses and flaws? Why? 2 Corinthians 12:9-10.

5. What light does 1 Corinthians 1:26-31 shed on God's choice of people who are not "ideal"?

6. God uses ordinary people with limitations and weaknesses. According to 2 Corinthians 4:6-7 NIV*, how does this bring glory to him?

7. Often we are dissatisfied with the way God made us because we feel it lowers other people's estimation of us. In God's sight how significant is earthly status or appearance? Galatians 2:6 AMP*; 1 Samuel 16:7.

8. God wants us to place significance on spiritual responses and qualities. What should we dwell on rather than human appearance and abilities? Why? 2 Chronicles 16:9; 1 Corinthians 13:1-3; 1 Peter 3:4.

9. Consider Jeremiah 9:23-24. In place of "boast of" or "glory in," use the words "bask in"—as a husband or wife basks in loving admiration, or a soloist in lavish applause. How much are you tempted to feel significant or secure because of the things listed in verse 23? In what ways do these things occupy your thoughts or your conversation?

   Write out verse 24 in your own words.

Optional:
In ancient as in modern days, many people tried to find their identity through glorying in their connections with people whom they evaluated as superior. (See 1 Corinthians 1:11-12.) In 1 Corinthians 3:21-4:5, Paul gives a better basis for a sense of worth, and helpful insights into evaluating oneself or other people. What does he say about the following:
a. God's appraisal of who you are:

b. Principles for a true evaluation:

Optional (continued)

When evaluating you, God disregards human merit and ratings. He bases his assessment on his unmerited favor toward you—on all you are and have in your union with his Son. You are his prized possession, on whom he has bestowed boundless spiritual blessings and resources. You are "somebody who has everything." This can provide security and confidence, enabling you to live a godly life and serve him faithfully.

God's approval of you as his child is settled and invariable. But his approval of your performance as his servant can change. How can you affect his assessment of your works? 1 Corinthians 4:2; 2 Timothy 2:15.

10. Review the Scriptures in this study. What incorrect thoughts or feelings about God and myself have I been holding?

What specific things about myself do I dislike or feel ashamed of?

What things do I take the credit for or feel superior about?

Pause and talk these things over with God. Tell him exactly how you feel. Then by faith thank him for his love and wisdom in giving you each negative quality, and offer him the credit and glory for each humanly desirable aspect of your person. Do this whenever the old negative or proud feelings arise. Begin asking him each day to work in you a deep sense of self-esteem that centers in him.

If I believe God failed in major or minor ways when he gave me my body, mind, and basic abilities, it hinders my trust in his plan for my life.

As the author and director of the drama of my life, God has given me a body and personality especially qualified to reveal him in a unique way. When I refuse to accept myself and my role, I am pushing God aside and demonstrating on the stage of my life an untrue picture of him. If I am negative toward myself, I portray him as an unwise creator, who is untrustworthy and unable to make something significant out of my life. If I am independent or proud, I give the impression that God is of minor importance. I have the freedom to present a distorted picture of God through my life if I want to, but it dishonors him and means immeasurable loss to me.

11. Write a *Brief Statement of Truth* about something that impresses you in this study. Use it frequently to promote a humble-yet-confident acceptance of yourself.

Favorite Passages

Notes and Quotes. *Add your own as you discover them.*

Sample:

The more we get what we now call "ourselves" out of the way and let Him take us over, the more truly ourselves we become . . . . He made us. He invented—as an author invents characters in a novel—all the different men that you and I were intended to be. In that sense our real selves are all waiting for us in Him. It is no good trying to "be myself" without Him. The more I resist Him and try to live on my own, the more I become dominated by my own heredity and upbringing and surroundings and natural desires. In fact what I so proudly call "Myself" becomes merely the meeting place for trains of events which I never started and which I cannot stop . . . . I am not, in my natural state, nearly so much of a person as I like to believe; most of what I call "me" can be very easily explained. It is when I turn to Christ, when I give myself up to His Personality, that I first begin to have a real personality of my own.

—C.S. Lewis,
Mere Christianity

6. God's Plan and My Past

How far back into the past does God's plan for us extend? When did God begin to exert his loving sovereignty over the factors that have shaped us?

As you meditate on the Scriptures in this study, copy the most meaningful Bible portions into the *Favorite Passages* section on page 52.

1. Before you begin to study, pray that you will see more clearly how your past relates to God's plan, and that your attitudes toward people and events in your background will more and more please the Lord.

> *Prayer is always the preface of blessing . . . the forerunner of mercy.*
> —Charles H. Spurgeon

2. What do you learn from Ephesians 1:4 and Jeremiah 31:3 about the Lord's heart involvement with his people and when it began?

3. What does Psalm 139:16 LB* say about my whole life, including my past?

4. When did God set Jeremiah apart for his mission in life? Jeremiah 1:5.

5. How far back is God actively present in the lives of his people? Psalm 71:6; Isaiah 46:3.

6. In Daniel 2:21 and Acts 17:26-27, what do you learn about a) God's influence in world history; b) His purpose in the way he has guided it?

   How might this apply to my personal history, since my life and my destiny have always been in his hands?

7. God does not fill our background (including our formative years) with only desirable happenings and influences. Describe briefly the background of *one* of the following people. Include the disadvantages, setbacks, and traumatic

experiences of his or her earlier life. How do you feel these helped prepare the person for a significant part in God's plan?

Moses: Exodus 1:8-3:1; Acts 7:17-36; Hebrews 11:23-26.
Ruth: Ruth 1-2, and 4:13-17.
Samuel: 1 Samuel 1-2.
Daniel: Daniel 1-6.
Jesus: Matthew 1-2; Luke 2; John 1:46, and 7:5.

8. Man has fallen and the world is in rebellion against its creator. Many negative, destructive influences exist in and around us. Things have befallen us that are deeply hated by a holy God and contrary to his expressed will, for he delights in lovingkindness, justice, and righteousness. When we are tempted to resist God because we do not understand why he allowed various things in our past, what should we remember? Romans 11:33-34 PH*.

9. Though God does not always explain things to us, he has always felt our distresses deeply. What were his feelings about the oppression and affliction of his people in Exodus 3:7, 16 NASB* and Isaiah 63:9?

Often our "why's" about our past are settled (though perhaps not answered) when we meditate on a counter-question: "Why did God let his Son suffer beyond imagining?" He bore all the griefs of every year of my life. He carried all the sorrows felt by every person in every city, village, or rural area, in all the world throughout the centuries. On the cross he took upon himself the sins of every person ever born; he experienced all our guilt. How immense a weight of anguish fell on him! If he suffered so much for me, can I not trust him with my past, with its hurts and its guilt?

10. Meditate word by word on Isaiah 53:4-5 and record the thoughts that most impress you as to what Christ bore, how much he suffered, and why.

11. According to the prophecy in Isaiah 61:1-3 (quoted by Christ in Luke 4:18-19), what did Jesus come to do for each of us personally?

12. God's plan includes victory over past traumas or failures that nag at us or hobble us today. We can fortify ourselves to overcome the past by developing a stronger sense of who God is—his loving acceptance of us, his deep involvement in our lives, his total forgiveness, his wisdom, his sovereign power, and his gracious purposes.

    A good place to begin is the parable of the prodigal son in Luke 15:11-32. Here Jesus describes how God the Father feels toward each of us, regardless of what our past (recent or distant) may have held. Read the parable, giving special attention to verses 17-24. Mark the parts that especially show the warmth of God's unconditional love and the fullness of his forgiveness.

    Take ten or fifteen minutes to prayerfully meditate on other passages about God's attitude toward you; possible verses are Isaiah 43:4, Psalm 103:11-14, and Romans 8:1, 33-34 PH*. It may help to review your *Favorite Passages* in this study and the previous ones. Jot down below two verses that help you the most in accepting yourself and your past—or in being humbly realistic before God if you tend to feel superior about yourself or your background.

Reference	Key Thought

If you find it particularly difficult to accept your past or to overcome feelings of superiority, Appendix A, "Giving God My Past," may be helpful. See page 98.

The Jade Carver

A Chinese jade carver finds a priceless piece of jade—with a major flaw. He could try to hide the flaw. Instead he carefully studies it and plans an exquisite carving, making the defect central in a perfect design.

God did this for Joseph's brothers back in Genesis. In malice they sold their brother into a life of slavery in a distant land and almost brought their father to his grave by their lies about it. Through much suffering God brought them to a place of repentance. But he did more. He utilized their very failure to save multitudes of people, including themselves, from death through famine. He took the blackest fragment of their lives and made it central in a beautiful picture of salvation for themselves, for Joseph, for their entire family.

This is what God did at Calvary. He took man's greatest failure, his most shameful atrocity—putting to death the Son of God—and made it central in a perfect picture of salvation, available to all mankind. He can do this today for us. He is not pleased when we waste our lives by lamenting our failures or handicaps. He wants us to rely on him to forgive, to overrule, and to transform.

6. God's Plan and My Past (continued)

Through each of our lives, God wants to dramatize how loving and powerful he is, how sufficient to meet needs. Using our backgrounds and the influences he has allowed to touch us, he has created for each of us a stage exactly suited for the ways he wants to reveal himself through us. If I want my life story to unfold freely for his glory and my highest good, I must accept the stage and backdrop he has provided. Until I choose to believe that he was loving and wise in permitting my past, I will fail to experience and reveal him accurately today.

1. In the Scriptures God used people from a great variety of backgrounds to accomplish his will and glorify him. He used poorly educated fishermen, highly educated statesmen, despised foreigners, and noblewomen. He used a slave, a prisoner, a prince, a captive exile, a harlot, a herdsman, a seamstress, a shepherd, and a despised hireling of a colonial government. According to Galatians 3:26-29 and Colossians 3:11, what were some of the backgrounds of people in the early church; yet what was true of them all in Christ?

Optional:

The life of Joseph is a striking example of how God uses past events—including the mistakes and sins of other people—to prepare us to fulfill his purposes. Read his story in Genesis 37; 39-41; 44:14-46:27; 50:1-26; and Psalm 105:16-22. What disturbing situations did Joseph go through? List the references and key thoughts of two or three verses that especially show God's sovereignty in Joseph's going to Egypt and his purpose in all that happened.

2. God can use even our mistakes and failures for our good and his glory. Consider Saul the persecutor who became Paul the Apostle—Acts 22:1-5; 26:9-23; 1 Corinthians 15:9-10. What had God allowed Saul to be and do before he was converted?

What changed him—and how thoroughly?

3. In 1 Timothy 1:12-16 what do you learn about Paul's past and how God took advantage of it?

4. What in his past could have made Paul feel self-confident in the wrong way? What did he decide about his human advantages and confidence in them? Acts 22:3, 25-27; Philippians 3:3-9, 14.

5. Read Psalm 66:8-12.
   What troubles could these people look back on?

   What was God's purpose in these difficulties?

   What had he done for them during their trials and afterwards?

   Can you think of similar difficult things in your past that have already worked out favorably? Can you think of other things that still seem unacceptable to you and cause inner conflicts and negative reactions?

   There are no diamonds without heavy pressure and enormous heat. —W.T. Purkiser

6. Because we serve a great and powerful God who is able to work all things together for good, our past does not have to hinder us. The thing that determines whether it will be a curse or a blessing is our heart attitude. As you review the examples in this study and consider the following verses, fill in the chart below. 1 Corinthians 1:26-31; James 1:9-10 WMS*.

Attitudes that can make our past a hindrance	*Attitudes that can make our past a help*

Note: Review Study 4, "Why God Includes Trials," considering how it applies to your past.

7. What attitudes toward people can bind us, and what contrasting attitudes does God want? Romans 12:17-21; Ephesians 4:31-32.

Attitudes that hinder	Attitudes that please God

8. Choose the verse or passage in this study that most encourages you to accept your past and trust God to use it for your good and his glory. Write a *Brief Statement of Truth* to memorize and use in times of need.

God's plan for each of us is utterly realistic as well as good. It embraces all of our past, from year zero to now, including the ways people have failed us or mistreated us. Before we existed God foresaw our opportunities and misfortunes, our advantages and disadvantages, our strengths and shortcomings, our aptitudes and handicaps, our successes and failures. He knew before time began the ways we would resist him and the ways we would yield, the days, years, and decades we would waste, and the ones we would invest well. The whole drama of our lives has always been in his mind. So in his planning he has woven in all eventualities. Before time began he knew how he could use for good each negative chapter or paragraph of our lives. As we yield to him, he transforms them (often in unexpected ways) into something beautiful and useful. Even when we must continue to reap for what we have sown in the past, he incorporates those consequences into our life story in ways that glorify him and enrich us.

Whatever our past, the profitable way to view God's plan is "from now on." Whether or not I followed him yesterday or last year—or ten minutes ago—I can choose his best for this moment and trust him to guide me into his perfect will from now on.

Favorite Passages

Notes and Quotes. *Add your own as you discover them.*

Sample:

God accepts us as we are, but longs for us to become more. When we learn to cooperate with Him and seek His will as the supreme good of our lives, then we can believe what He already believes about us—that we can be vastly more than we are. We need not forever be the victims of our earlier conditioning. God has put within us the power to change, to overcome handicaps, and to grow.

(Adapted from The Art of Understanding Yourself *by Cecil Osborne.)*

7. God's Plan for My Development

God envisions for each of us an attractiveness, vitality, and adequacy that far surpasses our highest expectations for ourselves. Whatever we have attained spiritually and morally, we still fall short of the glorious, loving ideal he has in mind for us. More than we know (and perhaps in different ways than we think) our potentiality has been stifled, and our personalities inhibited, by sin.

Whatever our present state of development, God is neither disillusioned with us nor content for us to remain as we are. He wants to liberate us more and more from cords of hostility, resentment, self-blame, regrets, anxiety, fear, and feelings of inferiority or superiority. His plans for us include the realization of our personal uniqueness plus an excellence of character beyond the reach of our human powers.

> *He made me a polished arrow (Isaiah 49:2 RSV). Now we know that sticks are not by nature arrows; they do not grow so, but they are made so; by nature they are knotty and rugged, but by art they are smooth and handsome.*
> —George Swinnock (1627-1673)

As you meditate on the Scriptures in this study, copy the portions that mean most to you into the *Favorite Passages* section on page 61.

1. Ask God to enlighten you about his plan to develop your full potential by bringing you to the "completeness of personality found in Christ."

> *In God's name, I beseech you, let prayer nourish your soul as meals nourish your body!*
> —Francis Fenelon

2. Reflect on the following verses and record in the chart below what you discover on each subject. Ephesians 4:13-16; Colossians 1:9-12; 1 Thessalonians 5:23-24; Hebrews 13:20-21 (chart continued on next page).

God's goals for my development	How these will be accomplished

54

God's goals for my development	How these will be accomplished

3. In his deep wisdom, God has planned for us to share his glory in a growing way now, not just in eternity. Read 1 Corinthians 2:6-13, alert to how it relates to you and your spiritual progress. Then answer the following:

What is true of God's intentions for your development and fulfillment? (2:7-9).

What has God provided so that you can know and enjoy the spiritual blessings he has given you to possess? (2:10-13).

From before all time He was concerned for our well-being, and planned the gospel that we should enter into our glory . . . The glories that come to believers are not haphazard, but are in accordance with God's plan from of old . . . When men first believe they do not all at once grasp the full implications of the faith. At first all are 'babes.' But the way to advance is open to everyone. There is no spiritual truth that is not available for even the humblest believer to appropriate.

—Leon Morris, from *1 Corinthians,*
Tyndale New Testament Commentaries

4. What is the Lord doing in us as we cooperate? Who accomplishes this? What is our part? 2 Corinthians 3:17-18.

God has a natural law in force to the effect that we are conformed to that upon which we center our interest and love.

—Miles Stanford,
Green Letters

5. Perhaps you find yourself enslaved to specific sins, or to a lifestyle that does not please God. What is his plan to release you from this bondage? John 8:31-32, 36; Psalm 119:45.

6. Complacency about sin can arrest our development. Read Proverbs 1:22-23, 29-33, and James 4:1-7, 11-17, asking the Lord to speak to you personally. Write down what he shows you about the following:

a. Things that motivate you to greater obedience.

b. Specific sins you have been casually tolerating or struggling against with little success.

7. As believers, we are God's garden, God's building. According to 1 Corinthians 3:11-15, what does he want built into our lives? Why do you think he used these particular words?

In contrast, if we go through life ignoring God's will and provisions, what do we build into our lives and into other people? Why are these materials unsuitable?

Optional:
The Old Testament uses many illustrations to describe God's plans to develop Israel as a nation and Jerusalem as a city. We can apply these to our spiritual lives as his people, the "true Israel of God." From the following Scriptures, record the thoughts that most express what you want him to do in your life. Isaiah 51:3, 54:11-12, and 58:10-12; Ezekiel 16:13-14; Hosea 14:5-6.

8. God wants to develop in our lives inner qualities that in turn will influence our outer lives and actions. What are three characteristics he especially wants to cultivate in us? 1 Corinthians 13:13; 1 Thessalonians 1:3.

In the following definitions of positive and negative qualities, underline the parts that stand out to you.

Faith—Trust in God and what he has said in his word; dependence on him as the ultimate source of all we need emotionally, physically, materially, and socially (whether his provision comes directly from him or through human channels).

Love—Giving of ourselves to God and to other people, wanting their best and seeking to meet their needs whether or not they reward us with the service, recognition, or appreciation that we want.

Hope—Confident expectation of future realities and blessings in this life and the next; assurance that God's final chapter will right all wrongs and reward us beyond all we could ask or think.

God's plan leads us to true maturity, where our deepest needs are met as he develops these qualities in us. Our own plans keep us on some lower and unsatisfying level of emotional development, characterized by:

Misplaced faith—**a)** Undue dependence on other people to make our decisions, meet our needs, and form our opinions; dependence on their approval or attention for our emotional support. Or, **b)** undue dependence on ourselves, on our own ideas and our ability to control people and circumstances to get what we want; a distrust of others and a lack of cooperation with them.

Deficient love—Giving of ourselves conditionally to others, ready to meet their needs only if and when they meet ours.

False hope—Unrealistic expectation of finding some personal earthly utopia, some perfect situation or ideal person to meet all our needs—resulting in disenchantment or cynicism when such a hope is disappointed; hope set more on earthly satisfaction than on spiritual and eternal gain.

9. Pray over this study, asking God to search your heart and life and show you specific ways he wants you to grow. Record the things he shows you and pray about them daily for a week. Select one point for specific action.

Strive to get beyond mere pensive longing. Set your face like a flint and begin to put your life in order.

—A.W. Tozer,
Gems from Tozer

Do not pray for easier lives;
Pray to be stronger men.
Do not pray for tasks equal to your powers;
Pray for powers equal to your tasks.
Then your life shall be no miracle,
But you shall be a miracle.
Every day you shall wonder
At that which is wrought in you by the grace of God.
—Phillips Brooks

57

7. God's Plan for My Development (continued)

God never hurries. He takes his time in developing us for our earthly calling as well as for eternity. Moses was 80 when he began his major task, and his preparation included 40 years of oblivion in the wilderness. After David was chosen and anointed to be king, God groomed him for thirteen years as he wandered about hiding in caves to escape capture and death. After God removed his opponent, one of the twelve tribes of Israel crowned him king; it took seven more years before the whole nation accepted him. Consider also the apostle Paul. We read little about him until fourteen years after his conversion, when at about the age of 48 he was launched into his life's work. Even in our age of rapid change and instant everything, God continues to prefer quality rather than speed in developing his people.

When God wants to make an oak, he takes a hundred years, but when he wants to make a squash, he takes six months.

—Dr. A.H. Strong

1. The following verses give some principles for progress. List the things that can hinder or help our development.

References	Hindrances to development	Helps to development
2 Peter 3:17-18		
1 Peter 2:1-2		
1 Peter 5:5-10		
1 Corinthians 14:20		
Optional: Hebrews 12:1-15		

2. When Paul wrote Philippians he was about 60 years old and had followed Christ for at least 30 years. How did he feel about his progress and his goal? Philippians 3:12-14.

3. Consider Philippians 1:6 LB,* Philippians 3:20-21, and Jude 24 LB*. What insights do you get about what God has in mind for us and when?

   Does any truth in these verses especially increase your confidence or motivate you to press on with greater singleness of heart?

Optional:
A common feeling among Christians is that we must be nearly finished products, models of perfection, in order to feel acceptable or serve Christ effectively. What do the verses in Questions 2 and 3, 1 John 1:8, 10 and James 3:2, say to this point? How do you think this misconception hinders our development and outreach?

Can you think of any cross references or illustrations from Scripture for this question and the preceding one?

4. How do some of us feel at times because of our failures and lack of progress? Psalm 73:21-22.

5. If we feel discouraged with ourselves and our development, what truths can encourage us? Psalm 73:23-26.

6. Whether we are discouraged or encouraged about our performance and progress, what perspective does the Lord want us to have? 1 Corinthians 4:4-5.

   In any building or remodeling, progress often means that things look worse before they look better. God's view of us reaches far beyond present appearances to the final result. When by faith we step back and see things from his viewpoint, he transforms our attitude so that we rejoice in eventually attaining his glorious ideal for us. "We confidently and joyfully look forward to actually becoming all that God has had in mind for us to be" (Romans 5:2 LB).

7. What important truth about ourselves can we learn more clearly through our failures, discouragements, and yearnings to please God more? Romans 7:18-19; 2 Corinthians 3:5.

8. Why is this view of ourselves important in our experience of God and his work in us? James 4:6; Isaiah 57:15.

9. What twofold realization can rescue us from the stress and impotence of our fruitless efforts to perfect ourselves?
   a) The source of virtues and power I need—Philippians 1:11, 2:13.

   b) My simple part in experiencing these—2 Corinthians 5:7.

In our frustrated attempts to mold ourselves into Jesus' image, let us ask ourselves, "Am I the potter or the clay? The sculptor or the marble?" Our efforts, though unfruitful, prove worthwhile if we learn the lesson that shouts at us from a thousand failures, "Even your best efforts cannot defeat sin in your life and produce godly virtues." But we must never stop there. We must go on to listen to the good news the Spirit brings, "Christ is your life; through him you partake of the very nature of God. Let him live his life in you. Let him mold you and use you."

As we rely on Christ and behold him long and often, we discover a new ability quietly developing in us, the ability to emulate our beloved Father, whom we were created to resemble. This comes through the outshining of Christ in us, who is the brightness of the Father's glory and the exact representation of his person. The secret of being Christlike lies in Christ, "Christ, in you, the hope of glory" (Colossians 1:27).

> *I have striven in vain to abide in Him. I'll strive no more. For has He not promised to abide with me—never to leave me, never to fail me? . . . I am one with Christ. It was all a mistake to try and get the fullness out of Him. I am part of Him. Each of us is a limb of His body, a branch of the vine. Oh, think what a wonderful thing it is to be really one with a risen Savior.*
>
> —Hudson Taylor,
> from *Hudson Taylor and Maria*, by John Pollock

Optional:
God's plan for us includes a delicate blend of faith and discipline. His working in us as we trust him is the indispensable basis; but this does not mean that Christian virtues are produced automatically with no conscious cooperation on our part. Our task is to "look unto Jesus," resting not on our own powers but on him and his promises. Beginning with this basic attitude of faith, what does God ask us to do to assure further growth? 2 Peter 1:4-8; 2 Corinthians 7:1 (see next page).

Optional, continued

"I exert all my strength in reliance upon the power of Him who is mightily at work in me."
Colossians 1:29 WEYM

It is not a present experience that ensures fruit unto maturity, but a patient continuance in well doing. . . . Fruit ripens slowly; days of sunshine and days of storm each add their share. Blessing will succeed blessing, and storm follow storm before the fruit is full grown or comes to maturity.

—George Goodman

When God wants to drill a man,
And thrill a man,
And skill a man,
When God wants to mold a man
To play the noblest part;
When He yearns with all His heart
To create so great and bold a man
That all the world shall be amazed,
Watch His methods, watch His ways!
How He ruthlessly perfects
Whom He royally elects!
How He hammers him and hurts him,
And with mighty blows converts him
Into trial shapes of clay which
Only God understands;
While his tortured heart is crying
And he lifts beseeching hands!
How He bends but never breaks
When his good He undertakes;
How He uses whom He chooses,
And with every purpose fuses him,
By every act induces him
To try His splendor out—
God knows what He's about!
—V. Raymond Edmond,
The Disciplines of Life

Our worth to God as his children is incalculable and fixed. Our value as his servants can increase manyfold. "A bar of steel worth five dollars, when wrought into horseshoes, is worth ten dollars. If made into needles, it is worth three hundred and fifty dollars; if into penknife blades, it is worth thirty-two thousand dollars; if into springs for watches, it is worth two hundred and fifty thousand dollars. What a drilling the poor bar must undergo to be worth this! But the more it is manipulated, the more it is hammered, and passed through the fire, and beaten and pounded and polished, the greater the value."

—Author unknown

God is well able to transform men into servants who are satisfactory. —J.B. Phillips

Favorite Passages

Notes and Quotes. *Add your own as you discover them.*

Sample:
The capacity for Christ's indwelling is elastic: it increases as the years go by . . . we are filled only to the amount of our capacity. There is always more of His fullness as the years unfold . . . For the greater the obedience, the greater the discipline, the greater the faith, the fuller and more complete the allegiance to our precious Lord—the more does the heart expand to receive more and more of Jesus.''

—Alan Redpath,
Victorious Christian Living

62

8. God's Plan and My Future

As you study this topic, note the verses or phrases of Scripture that most encourage you to trust God's plan for you and to face the future with realism and confident hope. Copy these verses in your *Favorite Passages* section.

1. Pray that you will sense more fully the goodness of God's intentions for your future, and that you will fit wholly into his plan for you all the days of your life.

   "So I say to you, Ask and keep on asking, and it shall be given you; seek and keep on seeking, and you shall find . . . ." (Luke 11:9 AMP).

2. In the following verses, what inspires a confident attitude toward God and the future? Psalm 23:6; Psalm 31:14-15 HAR*; Jeremiah 29:11.

3. As you read and consider Psalm 121, which promises most encourage you?

Optional:
In every difficulty your future may hold, assured deliverance is your legacy as you trust God. From the following Scriptures, fill in the chart below. Psalm 50:15, Psalm 62:1-2, 7 MOF*; Psalm 91:1-6; 1 Corinthians 10:13; 1 Thessalonians 1:10; Hebrews 2:14-15.

Deliverances that God promises you	Responses that lead to deliverance

The passage I like best, and why

4. What will be true of me as I grow old? Isaiah 46:4; Psalm 92:14-15.

5. Of what else can I be sure if I trust God and follow his plan?

   a. Philippians 4:13 AMP*

   b. Proverbs 4:18

   c. 2 Timothy 4:8

6. From 1 Thessalonians 4:15-18 and 2 Thessalonians 1:8-10 PH*, what do you learn about the end times? Summarize what will happen and describe what it will mean to you.

7. What are some of God's desires and promises for my ultimate future? John 17:24; Revelation 21:1-4, and 22:3-4.

8. What does God plan to do for me throughout all eternity? Ephesians 2:7.

9. Go back over your answers above and your *Favorite Verses* and describe the ways they affect your thoughts and feelings about God, yourself, and the future.

False thoughts and negative feelings that these truths counteract	*Positive feelings and responses that these truths produce*

Spend a few minutes praising God for these truths and what they mean to you.

Many songs and hymns encourage confidence in God's plans for our future. In the ones quoted below, mark the phrases that especially bless you.

> *If we could see beyond today*
> *as God doth see,*
> *If all the clouds should roll away,*
> *The shadows flee,*
> *O'er present griefs we would not fret,*
> *Each sorrow we would soon forget,*
> *For many joys are waiting yet*
> *For you and me.*
>
> *If we could see—if we could know—*
> *We often say,*
> *But God in love a veil doth throw*
> *Across our way.*
> *We cannot see what lies before*
> *And so we cling to Him the more.*
> *He leads us 'til this life is o'er.*
> *Trust and obey.*
>   —Author unknown
>
> *When our spirits, clothed immortal,*
> *Wing their flight to realms of Day,*
> *This our song through endless ages,*
> *Jesus led me all the way.*
>   —Fanny Crosby

ADDITIONAL EXPERIENCING GOD STUDY

8. God's Plan and My Future (continued)

1. God wants to meet our needs and lead us into a life of fulfilled desires for time and eternity. From the following passages, fill in the chart below. Psalm 91:14-16; Proverbs 23:17-18; Joshua 1:8; Proverbs 4:4-9[1]; Daniel 12:3; Romans 8:16-18 PH*.

How To Guarantee A Good Future	
What I should do	*What I can count on God to do*

2. As I follow the Lord, I can confidently expect God's blessing and enrichment. What can I also expect the future to hold, and why? 1 Peter 2:19-21; 2 Corinthians 4:10-11; 2 Timothy 3:12.

3. What things does Jesus promise us in John 16:33?

[1] Note: The wisdom referred to here is described in Proverbs 2:1-6 and Colossians 2:2-3.

The word "tribulation" in John 16:33 can also be translated "affliction," "trouble," or "pressure." It includes physical, mental, emotional, and spiritual pressures and sufferings. These are part of God's strategy for developing and enriching us.

Pressed out of measure and pressed to all length;
Pressed so intensely it seems beyond strength.
Pressed in the body and pressed in the soul;
Pressed in the mind till the dark surges roll.
Pressure by foes, and pressure by friends;
Pressure on pressure, till life nearly ends.

Pressed into loving the staff and the rod;
Pressed into knowing no helper but God.
Pressed into liberty where nothing clings;
Pressed into faith for impossible things.
Pressed into living a life in the Lord;
Pressed into living a Christ-life outpoured.
                                        —Author unknown

4. Though life will include suffering and loss, of what can I be confident?

   a. Psalm 138:7-8

   b. 2 Corinthians 1:3-5

   c. 2 Corinthians 4:15-18

5. When God's will involves leaving behind that which I treasure, what does he promise? Matthew 19:29-30.

6. If we could lift the veil and peer into our personal futures, what specific things might we see?	Yet what can we be sure of, whether we face extreme difficulties or ordinary ones?
Psalm 46:2-3	Psalm 46:1
Luke 21:25-26	Luke 21:27-28

Romans 8:35	Romans 8:37-39

7. God gives exciting promises for the future in Exodus 33:14, Isaiah 41:10, and Hebrews 13:5-6. In each passage he speaks of the best thing he could promise, plus some of the benefits that accompany it.

His best promise	*The accompanying benefits*

> *The man who has God for his treasure has all things in One. Many ordinary treasures may be denied him, or if he is allowed to have them, the enjoyment of them will be so tempered that they will never be necessary to his happiness . . . for he now has it all in One, and he has it purely, legitimately and forever.*
>
> —A.W. Tozer,
> *The Pursuit of God*

8. Write a brief statement about some truth in this study that motivates you to follow God confidently into the future. Memorize it and use it whenever doubts, fears, or reservations arise within you. The briefer the statement, the easier it will be to remember and use.

God asks of us a trusting, open-handed attitude toward a future that will contain both blessing and suffering. He asks that our hands be open to receive his sufficiency for every situation and to give freely to meet the needs of others. Such an attitude releases us from our ingrown insistence on plotting our own course and protecting our own interests. It leads us into truly liberated, expanding lives. "With hand outstretched to whatever lies ahead, I go straight for the goal—my reward the honour of my high calling by God in Christ Jesus" (Philippians 3:14 PH).

The future begins with the rest of today.

68

Favorite Passages

Notes and Quotes. *Add your own as you discover them.*

Samples:

Your crises and circumstances will be your pulpit. The deeper the crisis the higher the pulpit. —Ruth Paxon

God's way may be harder for you, but it will be easier on you. —Dr. Howard Hansen

O Lord, by all Thy dealings with us, whether of joy or pain, of light or darkness, let us be brought to Thee. Let us value no treatment of Thy grace simply because it makes us happy or because it makes us sad, because it gives us or denies us what we want; but may all that Thou sendest us bring us to Thee, that, knowing Thy perfectness, we may be sure in every disappointment that Thou art still loving us, and in every darkness that Thou art still enlightening us, and in every enforced idleness that Thou art still using us; yes, in every death that Thou art still giving us life, as in His death Thou didst give life to Thy Son, our Savior, Jesus Christ. Amen.

—Phillips Brooks

9. God's Plan and Why I Am Here

As we fit into God's plan for us, he unfolds exciting and challenging purposes for living. Choosing lesser purposes makes us misfits without true significance—no matter what level of achievement or fame we reach in people's eyes.

1. Before beginning, pray to know God in closer friendship and oneness, and to be involved in the purposes for which he created and redeemed you—"that you may stand firm, mature and fully convinced of all that is God's will for you" (Colossians 4:12 expanded).

2. In your *Favorite Passages* section, copy the verses below (or parts of them) that most impress you as to *why God has placed you on earth*. As you complete the rest of this study, add other Scriptures that especially speak to you about your purposes in life. Isaiah 43:7; Ephesians 1:5-6, 12, and 5:8, 10; 1 Peter 2:9.

3. Why is it appropriate that our lives revolve around the Lord and glorify him? Colossians 1:16-17; 1 Corinthians 6:19-20.

4. 2 Thessalonians 1:11 speaks of God's calling of us and his powerful working in us. Then in verse 12, what two-fold purpose for this does Paul give?

Optional:
"The chief end of man is to glorify God and to enjoy Him forever"(*Westminister Catechism*). God's intention, in turn, is to glorify *man* and to enjoy *him* forever! Prayerfully meditate on the following verses, writing down the thoughts that impress you on this subject. 1 Corinthians 2:7 NIV*; Colossians 3:4; 2 Thessalonians 2:14.

5. Review the above questions and your answers. Which verse or statement best summarizes God's goal for people?

6. In the verses below, note Paul's example of godly ambitions, and motivations, attitudes and actions, and fill in the chart.

Paul's ambitions and motivations	His resulting attitudes and actions
Philippians 1:20	Philippians 1:25
Philippians 3:8b, 10	Philippians 3:7-8a
Colossians 1:28b	Colossians 1:28a,29
Acts 20:24b	Acts 20:24a
2 Corinthians 5:9-10	
	2 Corinthians 5:11
2 Corinthians 5:14	
	2 Corinthians 5:15
2 Corinthians 5:18-19	
	2 Corinthians 5:20

How would you summarize Paul's goals for:
Believers?

The unsaved?

Himself?

7. King Solomon, who had every conceivable resource to draw on, sought to find fullness of life in knowledge, possessions, pleasures, and monumental achievements instead of God. What did he eventually conclude about life and its meaning? Ecclesiastes 1:8, 13-14, and 2:11.

> The world today is full of sufferers from the wasting disease which Albert Camus focused as Absurdism ('life is a bad joke'), and from the complaint which we may call Marie Antoinette's fever, since she found the phrase that describes it ('nothing tastes'). These disorders blight the whole of life: everything becomes at once a problem and a bore, because nothing seems worthwhile . . . . What makes life worthwhile is having a big enough objective, something which catches our imagination and lays hold of our allegiance; and this the Christian has, in a way that no other man has. For what higher, more exalted, and more compelling goal can there be than to know God?
> —J.I. Packer,
> Knowing God

8. Knowing God in a personal and intimate relationship should be the basic purpose of our lives, the root from which all our other goals stem. Write a short paragraph about why knowing God is such an essential and exciting goal. Jeremiah 9:23-24; Hosea 6:2, 6; John 17:3.

How should we pursue this goal? Proverbs 2:1-6; Philippians 3:8.

9. As you consider your peers, what are their most common goals?

How do you think these compare with the God-given goals you have been studying?

What goals in your life most easily conflict with pursuing God and his purposes for you?

Is God saying anything to you about these goals?

Be Thou my Vision, Oh Lord of my heart;
Nought be all else to me, save that Thou are—
Thou my best thought, by day or by night,
Waking or sleeping, Thy presence my light.

Riches I heed not, nor man's empty praise,
Thou mine inheritance, now and always:
Thou and Thou only, first in my heart,
High King of heaven, my Treasure Thou art.

—8th Century Irish hymn

9. God's Plan and Why I Am Here (continued)

1. God's purposes for us include a) the high privilege of a close relationship with him, b) the transformation of our characters, and c) the things he wants us to achieve. Summarize below what the verses say about each topic.

   My relationship with him—how he wants me to respond to him
   John 4:23; Mark 12:28-30; 1 Corinthians 1:9.

   My character and attitudes—how he wants to reveal himself through me
   Galatians 5:22-23; Romans 12:9-12; Ephesians 4:31-32.

   My service and achievements—what he wants to accomplish through me
   Ephesians 2:10; Matthew 4:19, and 25:34-40; Galatians 6:10; Romans 14:19.

Optional:
Consider again Mark 12:28-30. List and meditate on the ways we are to love God. Then describe or define what you think each one means. Under each point, can you think of any attitudes or actions that would enable you to love him more in that aspect of your relationship?

a.

b.

c.

d.

2. What great task, in which we can all have a part, is on Jesus' heart? Matthew 28:18-20; Luke 24:46-48; Acts 1:8.

3. What does God want to see in our lives? Why? Proverbs 11:30; John 15:8.

4. From Paul's prayer in Colossians 1:9-12, list the goals mentioned and the resources available to accomplish them.

Goals:

Resources:

Pray over Questions 1 through 4, asking that they will become part of your life.

Optional:

In winning, building, and training people throughout the world, God has specific purposes and tasks for each of us. In order to fulfill his distinctive purposes for our individual lives, we must use the unique gifts he has given us. Read through Romans 12:3-8 and 1 Corinthians 12. Begin to pray frequently that he will enable you to discover, develop, and fulfill the specific service for which he has gifted you.

As you serve him in various ways, be alert to the types of opportunities in which you experience his blessing and develop the greatest freedom. This can help you determine how he has gifted you. As you feel drawn to certain of these serving gifts, use the principles in Appendix B to clarify what gift or gifts God has given you.

5. What acts are significant in God's sight and honoring to him? 1 Corinthians 10:31; Colossians 3:17, 23-24.

Let us think of a Christian believer in whose life the twin wonders of repentance and the new birth have been wrought. He is now living according to the will of God as he understands it from the written Word. Of such a one it may be said that every act of this life is or can be as truly sacred as prayer or baptism or the Lord's Supper. To say this is not to bring all acts down to one dead level; it is rather to lift every act up into a living kingdom and turn the whole life into a sacrament, an external expression of an inward grace.

> . . . *Let us practice the fine art of making every work a priestly ministration. Let us believe that God is in all our simplet deeds and learn to find Him there . . . .* "Lord . . . I want to live so fully in the Spirit that all my thoughts may be sweet incense ascending to Thee and every act of my life may be an act of worship."
> —A.W. Tozer,
> *The Pursuit of God*

6. The following strategic opportunities to invest our lives are also open to every believer. What are they? Why do you think they are important?

Opportunity	Its importance
Matthew 9:36-38	
Ephesians 6:18-20	
2 Corinthians 9:6-9	
Galatians 6:6, 9	

Optional:
Consider 2 Corinthians 9:6-15, Matthew 6:19-21, Proverbs 19:17, and Acts 20:35. List as many reasons as possible for being generous.

The day will come when "the heavens will vanish in a tearing blast, the very elements will disintegrate in heat and the earth and all its works will disappear" (2 Peter 3:10 PH). Of the things we can give our hearts and lives to day after day, only three are eternal—God, his word, and people.

Whatever our earthly vocation, God wants us to have a heart for him, for his word, and for people. He deeply cares about the welfare (both temporal and eternal) of all people on earth, and he longs for a personal relationship with each one. As we come to know him and his word more and more, we store up in ourselves that which is eternal. We also learn to share his purposes, yielding fruit in two ways by: a) showing his character and compassion to meet people's needs and b) sharing his word to bring forth spiritual children and to help them invest their lives in the things that will last forever.

We will all receive God's warm welcome home as dear children; we will not all hear his "well done" as faithful servants.

The greatest use of life is to spend it for something that will outlast it.   —Emerson

7. As you review the purposes for which God has designed you, which verse or thought stands out to you in respect to each of the following:

   a. What can I be to God?

   b. What does he want to do in me?

   c. What does he want to do through me?

8. Prayerfully choose one point in Question 7 that should have higher priority in your life. Then decide on a specific action you want to take or a new life pattern you want to begin.

> *Be strong!*
> *We are not here to play, to dream, to drift.*
> *We have hard work to do, and loads to lift.*
> *Shun not the struggle—face it; 'tis God's gift.*
>
> *Be strong!*
> *It matters not how deep-entrenched the wrong,*
> *How hard the battle goes, the day how long.*
> *Faint not—fight on! Tomorrow comes the song.*
> —Babcock

Favorite Passages

Notes and Quotes. *Add your own as you discover them.*

Sample:

In this fallen world, we live in a smog of meaninglessness surrounded by high cliffs of self-choosing. Even with our most strenuous efforts to reach the highest of our independent goals, we cannot scale those cliffs and break free. Only God can lift us out. His commands and leadings provide the means by which his grace and power can rescue us. As we trust and obey, he lifts us ever higher into the invigorating atmosphere of his purposes for us.

10. God's Plan and My Response

As you meditate on the Scriptures in this study, copy into the *Favorite Passages* section on page 83 the verses or phrases that impress you most.

1. Pray that God will enable you to bring him joy by the way you respond to his broad plan for your life and his specific plan for each situation.

   It is to strong desire and constraining prayer that God will most assuredly manifest Himself.
   —Andrew Murray

2. What three things does God ask of us in order that we may experience his good, pleasing and perfect plan? Romans 12:1-2. Elaborate briefly on each of these points, perhaps using other translations and a dictionary.

3. What do you think are the major lessons Christ wants to teach us in John 12:24-26?

4. Look up each of the following verses, and put its reference beside the statement it best fits. *Pray over each, that it will be the actual response of your heart day by day.* Underline the statements that most speak to you.
   Matthew 6:33; Luke 9:23; Luke 14:33; Philippians 4:11-12; 2 Timothy 2:3.

   a. Give up all right to myself and "die daily" in order to be wholly Christ's and learn from him. _____

   b. Give up my personal claim to everything I have, considering it to be the Lord's, placing all at his disposal. _____

   c. Give Christ and his kingdom first place in my loyalties, not being anxious about my needs. _____

   d. Be ready to endure hardship for Christ. _____

   e. Be ready to adjust with contentment to whatever plan God has for me at various times, whether it be plentiful provision, simple living, or even poverty. _____

Acts 20:23-24; Philippians 3:7-8; Philippians 3:10; 1 Peter 2:11; 1 John 2:15-16.

f. Refuse to love what the world offers—comfort and physical gratification, the things my eyes crave for, the desire to be somebody in other people's estimation.   _____

g. Refrain from the lusts and overindulgences that damage me spiritually and emotionally.   _____

h. Consider all possible personal gain as rubbish compared with the priceless privilege of knowing Christ.   _____

i. Refuse to be troubled about possible danger, considering my life completely expendable to accomplish his purposes.   _____

j. Be determined to know and experience him more fully, pressing on to share not only his mighty resurrection power but also his sufferings and even to "die" in any way he has in mind for me.   _____

> I heard His call, "Come, follow!"
>   That was all.
> My gold grew dim,
> My soul went after Him,
> I rose and followed;
>   That was all.
> Who would not follow
> If they heard Him call?
>   —William R. Newell

> *God is not with our natural life while we pamper it; but when we resolutely put it out in the desert and keep it under, then God will be with it; and He will open up wells and oases, and fulfill all his promises for the natural.*
>   —Oswald Chambers

5. What attitudes and reactions does 1 Corinthians 9:24-27 command?

6. If I sense I am unwilling to follow God's plan for my life, what can I ask him to do? Philippians 2:13.

One way to pray this is, "Lord, make me willing to be willing."

Optional:
Read Matthew 26:37-44. Jot down what you observe about Jesus' struggles, including such things as: How did Jesus feel that night about God's plan? Was he able to resolve his struggles in a few moments? What did he ask for? Yet in spite of his feelings, what did he choose?

> *Father, I want to know Thee, but my coward heart fears to give up its toys. I cannot part with them without inward bleeding, and I do not try to hide from Thee the terror of the parting. I come trembling, but I do come. Please root from my heart all those things which I have cherished so long and which have become a very part of my living self, so that Thou mayest enter and dwell there without a rival. Then shalt Thou make the place of Thy feet glorious. Then shall my heart have no need of the sun to shine in it, for Thyself wilt be the light of it, and there shall be no night there. In Jesus' Name, Amen.*
> —A.W. Tozer,
> *The Pursuit of God*

7. Besides praying for God to mold my will to be like his, what can I do to assure that my mind and desires will be in line with his? Romans 8:5; Colossians 3:1-2.

8. What provisions can help us become more fully yielded and sanctified (set apart for God and his will alone)? John 17:17; 1 Peter 1:2.

9. According to Isaiah 1:19-20, we have two alternatives regarding God's plan for us. We can consent or refuse; we can obey or rebel. Mentally review the truths or Scriptures that you have studied in this chapter.

   a. What most motivates me to consent and obey?

   b. What most convinces me not to refuse and rebel?

10. Have you ever made the decisive choice to commit yourself fully to God and his plan for you? Commitment means to deposit your life in his account, to be available day by day for his use. Write below when and how you committed yourself wholly to the Lord, or write a prayer of commitment that you now want to offer. If you are facing a struggle with this, write a prayer telling the Lord how you feel and giving him permission to make you willing.

    Submitting to God means agreeing to exercise my freedom only within the liberating limits of his will.

ADDITIONAL EXPERIENCING GOD STUDY

10. God's Plan and My Response (continued)

You cannot surrender a life in an instant. That which is lifelong can only be surrendered in a lifetime.

—Jim Elliot

To enjoy God's good plan, we must make a decisive choice to give ourselves unreservedly to Christ. Then day by day, decision by decision, we must choose to yield to him and trust him. This requires watchfulness lest unscriptural attitudes or habits of thought and action edge their way back into our experience and rob us of the rich benefits of wholly following Christ.

1. What commonly held attitudes and false beliefs deny the goodness of the Lord and his devotion to our well-being? Isaiah 40:27 and 45:9-10; Psalm 73:11-14.

   Can you think of other attitudes or beliefs that hinder a positive response to God, either in biblical statements and illustrations, in life today, or in your own life?

   According to Jeremiah 11:20 and 12:3, the Lord "tries the feelings and the heart" and will "examine my heart's attitude toward Him" (NASB). Ask him to examine your thoughts and responses to him and what he permits to happen in your life. Though you may mentally agree that God is good, be alert for ways your faith needs more depth and constancy. Record below anything he brings to mind, now or later.

2. What impresses you about the attitudes of the people in:

   a. Habakkuk 3:17-18; Acts 16:23-25.

   b. Psalm 85:12, Psalm 147:11 LB*.

   c. Daniel 3:17-18.

3. Besides the attitudes shown above, what should my response include? Psalm 50:15 and 62:8.

Optional:
Notice in Psalm 77:1-10 how the psalmist formulated his feelings of perplexity at God's ways and voiced them to the Lord. Then he turned his thoughts to God's character, power, and mighty deeds, and began praising him and accepting the limits of his own mind in figuring out all God's ways (verses 11-20). What most impresses you in this Psalm?

When God's plan (either in what he allows to happen or in what he asks us to do) does not make sense to us, what should we remember? Isaiah 55:8-9.

God's mind resembles a vast ocean, mine a cup of water; his a huge computer, mine a small calculator. If I could comprehend all God's ways and reasons for acting, would he be great enough to deserve my worship?

4. Much of our resistance to God's will, in large or small matters, stems from a fear of some kind, such as:
   Fear that I will not get what I want out of life in such matters as vocation, marriage, location, possessions, security, status, popularity, recognition, ease, comfort, and pleasure.

   Fear that people will think I am odd, fanatical, and wasting my life.

   Fear of specific things I might have to do or be.

   Fear that I am not adequate to do his will—fear of failure.

   Fear that I will miss God's leading, that I will not be skilled enough to discern his will.

Write out the fears that might hinder you from yielding to God's perfect plan. Seek to be honest before God about your feelings. This can be difficult, especially for a strong person who may not see fear as an acceptable part of human experience. Fear can be one of the great prods to keep us trusting God; or if unfaced and unresolved, one of the great hindrances to enjoying his fellowship and doing his will.

My personal fears:

5. Seek the Lord's deliverance from the fears you have listed in Question 4. To equip yourself to combat these fears, think back on verses or promises you have studied that could help dispel them. Verses on fear might also help—such as 2 Kings 6:15-17, Psalm 27:1, Isaiah 41:10, 13 NASB*, 43:1-2, 51:12-13, Matthew 10:28-31, Hebrews 13:5-6. Indicate below several verses that help you dispel your specific fears.

6. Read Hebrews 11:1, 6 and 12:2. What simple basic response does the Lord ask of us? What do you discover about this inner act that especially interests you?

How then to have our faith increased? Only by thinking of all that Jesus is and all He is for us . . . He Himself as revealed in the Word to be the subject of our thoughts. Not a striving to have faith, but a looking off to the Faithful One seems all we need; a resting in the Loved One entirely, for time and for eternity.

—John McCarthy, as quoted in
Hudson Taylor's Spiritual Secret
by Dr. and Mrs. Howard Taylor

George Mueller, outstanding man of faith in the last century, gave this prescription for developing greater faith:

Be willing to pay the price. What price?
Study the Word of God and believe its blessed promises.
Be ready to say, "My whole life shall be one service for the living God."
Walk uprightly and don't regard iniquity in your heart.
With the simplicity of a child confide in God.
Feed your soul upon the Word of God and you will have an increase of faith in the measure that you exercise it.

George Mueller's faith was not a Jonah's gourd. It was of slow growth. It grew with increased familiarity with the Word of God; it flowered in an increased personal fellowship with God; and it came to fruition through trials, obstacles, difficulties and defeats—all of which he welcomed as so many stepping stones which his Heavenly Father affectionately placed in his life's pathway.

–*George Mueller Man of Faith*

7. Write a *Brief Statement of Truth* to use frequently in combating inner responses that could sabotage your commitment to God and your faith in his sufficiency.

Favorite Passages

Notes and Quotes. *Add your own as you discover them.*

Samples:
And shall I pray Thee change Thy will, my Father,
  Until it be according unto mine?
But no, Lord, no, that never shall be. Rather,
  I pray Thee, blend my human will with thine.

I pray Thee, hush the hurrying, eager longing.
  I pray Thee, quench the pangs of keen desire.
See in my quiet places wishes thronging—
  Forbid them, Lord. Purge, though it be with fire.

And work in me to will and do Thy pleasure.
  Let all within me, peaceful, reconciled,
Tarry content my Well-Beloved's leisure,
  At last, at last, even as a weaned child.
                    —Amy Carmichael

"He is no fool who gives what he cannot keep to gain what he cannot lose."
                    —Jim Elliot
            Through Gates of Splendor

11. God's Assured Guidance

What do you consult for guidance in your day-by-day choices? The opinions of other people? Your own ideas and preferences? Your feelings? Your scruples or rebellions? Your fears? Or even such things as television, popular authorities, or horoscopes? Are you driven to your choices by the need to be self-governing and to do your own thing? Do you make your choices by default, in a haphazard way, avoiding them as long as possible and eventually allowing events themselves to determine your decisions? Do you forge steadily ahead toward self-chosen goals and destinations?

Even the wisest human methods bypass the best in life—that exciting pilgrimage through prepared circumstances in company with the living God. The ruler of the universe, who knows each detail of the future, offers to be our personal guide into his plan for our highest good. He will lovingly impress his will on our minds if we walk with him in simple faith, opening ourselves to his ways of communicating.

1. As you begin to study, pray for a simple trust in God's unchanging eagerness to guide you into his good plan and away from tempting-but-treacherous bypaths. Ask him for greater clarity in discerning his will.

   Thy will—nothing more, nothing less, nothing else.

2. In your *Favorite Passages* section on page 91, copy the verses or phrases from the Scriptures below that most increase your confidence in God's readiness to guide you. Psalm 23:3 and 32:8-9; John 10:3-4; Psalm 139:9-12.

3. The following passages give three of the essentials for consistently knowing God's will. Psalm 119:105, 130; Proverbs 6:20-23; Romans 8:14; Galatians 5:16; Psalm 143:8, 10, and 25:4-5; James 1:5.

Three essentials	Observations concerning them
1.	
2.	
3.	

God's word is not so much a floodlight showing us the whole path; it is more like a torch throwing light on the next few steps.

4. Who qualifies for the Lord's teaching and guidance? Psalm 25:8-9, 12.

The good shepherd takes the initiative to lead his sheep. They do not have to beg him, secretly wondering *if* he will lead, but just ask for guidance with simple confidence and readiness to follow. This is the chief prerequisite, this willingness to do whatever he may ask because we believe he is good and wise. He does not ask us to blot out our desires so as to achieve an emotional neutrality, but simply to lay our desires at his feet, ready to do his will whether or not it coincides with our preferences.

The Lord does not *promise* to reveal his will to those who want to know it first and then decide whether or not they will do it. He is a leader of those bent on following, not a dispenser of useless information to the willful or curious. "If any man is willing to do His will, he shall know" (John 7:17). Jesus was speaking about doctrine, but the same principle applies to guidance.

5. Isaiah 42:16 can reassure us if we are afraid of missing God's leading. What things does he promise? To whom?

Think of the significance of each "I will" in this verse. When God says "I will," he who cannot fail is committing himself. Behind each commitment stands his faithful love and all-prevailing power. He *will* give us light, guide us, and influence us in countless ways so that we can do his will and receive his blessing—if we let him.

6. What do you learn from Isaiah 58:9-11 about guidance and blessing?

"Light accepted brings more light; light rejected brings the night." Sometimes we find it difficult to find God's will because we disregard what he has already shown us in general, or in a specific decision.

7. How might James 1:6-8 apply to a person who wavers between two opinions, not sure whether he will go God's way or his own?

Optional:
In Acts 16:7 the apostle Paul made a mistake in discerning God's will; the Lord showed him his error and redirected his steps. Likewise in 2 Corinthians 12:7-10, Paul mistook God's will in prayer and the Lord revealed his error. In contrast, he let the people in Psalm 106:13-15 have their way, to their detriment. Why? How did they differ from Paul in their heart attitudes?

8. Write out Revelation 3:7-8 in your own words and consider how the Lord can open and close doors of opportunity and circumstance in order to guide us.

   How might these truths, and Isaiah 30:21, encourage a person who truly wants God's will but is overly hesitant in making decisions for fear of taking a wrong turn?

9. Our security does not lie in having a detailed plan of the future handed to us, or in developing sleuth-like skill for detecting hidden clues as to what God's will is. What does Proverbs 3:5-6 prescribe and promise?

10. Which Scripture in this study do you find most helpful? Why?

The following poem can apply to any gate through which we pass into a new situation or opportunity or period of life.

> *And I said to the man*
> *Who stood at the gate of the year,*
> *"Give me a light, that I may tread*
> *Safely into the unknown."*
>
> *And he replied,*
> *"Go out in the darkness, and put your hand*
> *Into the hand of God.*
> *This shall be to you better than light*
> *And safer than a known way."*
>
> *So I went out,*
> *And finding the hand of God*
> *Trod gladly into the night.*
> *And He led me toward the hills*
> *And the breaking of Day in the lone east.*
>
> *So, heart, be still.*
> *What need our little minds,*
> *Our human minds, to know*
> *Since God has comprehension?*
> *In all the dizzy strife*
> *Of things both high and low*
> *God hides His good intention.*
>   —M.L. Haskins

11. God's Assured Guidance (continued)

Some people feel that if a course of action seems difficult or distasteful, it must be God's will; but if it is something they want to do, it must not be right. Many of the Scriptures studied in this book disprove this idea. Another position, a common modern view, says that how we feel or what we want is the most reliable basis for our decision—"If it feels good, do it."

1. What facts about my humanity make it dangerous merely to let my preferences guide me? Proverbs 14:12, 21:2, and 28:26; Ephesians 2:2-3; Galatians 5:17.

2. If I want my desires and judgments to become dependable indicators of God's guidance, more attuned to his will, what can I do? Psalm 37:4; John 15:7; Galatians 5:25 LB*.

3. What will help us see things from God's point of view and choose accordingly? Romans 12:2 PH*; Ephesians 4:23; Colossians 1:9.

   Besides learning God's commands, what do you think is involved in this?

Optional:
When God gave us common sense, he gave us a lot of leading. Write down your observations as to how this statement is true, both in big decisions and in small daily choices. What possible dangers lie in accepting this statement with no qualifications?

What qualities of life help make a person's thoughts and inclinations more trustworthy in guidance?

a. Proverbs 11:3	b. Proverbs 12:5
c. Proverbs 14:29	d. Proverbs 15:21

One sure way to miss God's way in the future is to choose a slightly divergent path today, compromising a little here, a little there. To avoid this, the habitual attitude of my life should be, "I do not seek My own will, but the will of Him who sent Me" (John 5:30). Some of us depend on our own wisdom and ignore God's little leadings. Then a large decision looms before us and in panic we try to determine God's will. Learning to discern and follow his will in our smaller decisions can prepare us for making right choices at the major crossroads.

If I fail to let God lead me in my daily living, I will miss much of his good plan for my life even if I happen to discover his will in the big decisions.

4. The book of Proverbs repeatedly shows that a wise man makes plans based on sound principles and careful observation of the factors involved, both spiritual and practical. What things characterize his approach to life and contribute to his ability to make good decisions in the following verses from Proverbs?

9:8	9:9	9:10
4:14-15	18:15	
21:5	22:3	

5. When making plans, what attitudes should we have according to:
   a. Psalm 25:14.

   b. Proverbs 16:3 NIV*.

   c. James 4:13-16.

   We are to use our God-given faculties to plan our way. In doing this we are to rely on him to give wisdom, to guide, to rule, and to overrule—then to direct our actual steps by further promptings, open or closed doors, interventions or interruptions.

6. What is another way to seek light the Lord may be giving? Proverbs 15:22 and 19:20.

   Counsel can be helpful or hindering, protective or misleading. We should seek it from people who themselves are obeying God's word and growing in grace and godliness.

7. According to Deuteronomy 18:10-14, Isaiah 8:19, 44:25, and 47:13-14;
   a. What should we avoid completely in making decisions?

b. Why is this so important?

"Many have gone a mile with Satan who never intended to go more than a couple of steps; but once in his company, they were unable to depart." Satan seduces people through astrology or the occult (even by accurate predictions at times), or curiosity, or a sense of power. Even genuine believers who have trifled with God's strict commands, dabbling with fortune telling, seances, or games such as the Ouija board, have opened themselves to eventual demonic oppression and bondage.

Optional:
Give one general command or principle that can help guide you in daily decisions. (For example, see Romans 12:17-18 NASB* regarding interpersonal relationships. God may lead contrary to the desires of other people, but we should at least carefully consider their ideas and feelings.)

8. When we feel we know better than God or get impatient, we risk making wrong or premature choices. Timing is often highly significant; for untimely choices, like wrong ones, can cause complications and distress. In Psalm 27:13-14, what counsel do we find for the temptation to be hasty?

> *Never act in a panic, nor allow man to dictate to thee. Calm thyself and be still. Force thyself into the quiet of thy closet until the pulse beats normally and the scare has ceased to disturb.*
>
> *When thou art most eager to act is the time when thou wilt make the most pitiable mistakes.*
>
> *Do not say in thine heart what thou wilt or wilt not do, but wait upon thy God until He makes known His way.*
>
> *So long as that way is hidden, it is clear that there is no need of action, and that He accounts Himself responsible for all the results of keeping thee where thou art.*
> —F.B. Meyer

9. As we follow the basic principles God has given for discerning his will, what important factor can help test our tentative choices? Colossians 3:15.

Colossians 3:15 is sometimes translated "Let the peace of Christ referee in your hearts . . ." When a rule has been broken in a football game, the referee blows his whistle to stop play and make the necessary adjustments before the game can resume. Similarly, a lack of peace about either large decisions or daily choices means we should stop and find out what has gone wrong—why there is a conflict in our hearts or with other people—before pressing ahead. To do this consistently some of us need to develop a greater awareness of our feelings and how we affect others.

> *This peace not only refers to individual tranquility of heart, but extends to peace among the members of the Body in their relations to one another.*
>
> —Kenneth S. Wuest

10. Think back over this study, and list three do's and three don'ts for guidance that help you most.

Do	Don't

Optional:

Consider the three people described below, and choose one or two Scriptures and thoughts you feel each person would most need in finding God's will.

a. A self-confident individual who has developed practical wisdom and considerable skill in making decisions:

b. A know-it-all person who is always right and who primarily wants to do his or her own thing:

c. A hesitant, vacillating person who finds each decision a major hurdle—the kind of person who might sit all morning trying to decide whether or not to get a haircut that day, finally flipping a coin rather than deciding.

God often varies his means of guidance from person to person, and from decision to decision. Do not feel he must guide you the same way he guides someone else. However, consistently overlooking some of the scriptural principles of guidance may hinder or sidetrack us. For example, if we depend entirely on the more subjective factors such as peace, our inner desires, and our impressions of the Spirit's leading, we easily fall prey to the deceitfulness of the flesh or the wiles of Satan. If we rely almost exclusively on external factors, such as providential circumstances, obvious opportunities, or counsel from leadership, we run the risk of ignoring specific light and personal conviction the Lord may want to give us through our intake of the word, the inner promptings of his Spirit, or our God-given gifts and inclinations.

As a safeguard against either extreme, God has provided both the subjective and the objective, both the internal and the external channels for tuning in to his guidance.

Note: See "Finding God's Will," Appendix B, page 101, for a summary of the major considerations in finding his will, and for key questions to ask yourself.

Favorite Passages

Notes and Quotes. *Add your own as you discover them.*

Samples:

. . . *the fundamental mode whereby our rational Creator guides His rational creatures is by understanding and application of His written Word . . . the true way to honour the Holy Spirit as our guide is to honour the Holy Scriptures through which He guides us . . . The Spirit leads within the limits which the Word sets, not beyond them. "He guideth me in the paths of righteousness"—but not anywhere else.*

—J.I. Packer,
Knowing God

Often we want to know God's will too soon. We want things mapped out in advance so we can plan with certainty. God wants us to keep our eyes on him, our hand in his, and our hearts content to say, "I know not what the future holds, but I know who holds the future . . ." He may show us his will at the last minute, but he never shows us too late.

12. Review Discovering God's Will

1. Pray that the Lord will open the eyes of your heart in new ways as you review the truths you have studied.

   The great point is to never give up until the answer comes . . . The great fault of the children of God is, they do not continue in prayer . . . they do not persevere. If they desire anything for God's glory, they should pray until they get it.
                                                                   —George Mueller,
                                                         George Mueller of Bristol

2. Think back over the preceding studies, using the table of contents to jog your thinking. From memory, write below your strongest impressions of how the studies have affected your life.

3. Now glance back over the questions and answers in each chapter, and record below several other verses or truths that have especially influenced your *inner* life—your thought life, your emotions, your understanding, or your trust in God and his plan.

Chapter title	Most helpful verse or truth

4. Choose an especially helpful verse that you have not yet committed to memory. Copy it on a card, memorize it, and review it every day for two or three weeks.

5. Has the Lord used this study to initiate any changes in your *outer* life—in relation to people? Situations? Responsibilities or activities? Jot down below the practical result that you feel is most significant. Pause and pray for grace to follow through on this more fully.

6. Write a brief summary of the truths you studied in each chapter.

Chapter	Brief summary
1.	
2.	
3.	
4.	
5.	
6.	
7.	
8.	
9.	
10.	
11.	

94

12. Review Discovering God's Will (continued)

"Let no man think he can have any measure of victory over his inner corruption without taking it to the Lord again and again in prayer."
                                                        —George Mueller

Conversely, let any person know that he can have a large measure of victory over inner corruption or disruption by taking it to him again and again in prayer. Do not ask out of a mere wishful longing, but with an expectation that God in his great goodness and power will work in you "both to will and to work for his good pleasure" (Philippians 2:13).

God's plan for me does not just include my major decisions. It includes the patterns of my daily living—my feelings, thoughts, actions, my choices, and priorities. It includes depending totally on God and finding my sufficiency in him day by day and hour by hour.

I constantly choose either to resist or to cooperate with God. Resisting can take the form of obvious rebellion or a subtle, unyielding spirit. I can detect this hidden resistance by noting negative thoughts, emotions, attitudes, bodily tension, unloving reactions, and undue reliance on my own efforts to get what I want (or even to do God's will).

1. In my daily living, what symptoms most often indicate that I may be resisting God and his plan?
   a. In my thoughts and emotions:

   b. In my attitudes toward God, myself or others:

   c. In my physical body:

   d. In my words and actions:

   Stop and pray for an awareness of these symptoms as soon as they occur in your life, and for grace to submit quickly to him and his plan. Pray about which truths and Scriptures will help you most to overcome them.

2. *For prayer and action*:
   From your applications in this book, select three or four changes in your life that need further attention. Record them in the following chart.
   Prayerfully decide on some simple, concrete steps you can take to make these applications more a part of your life in the weeks and months ahead. Assign a time to work on each one—maybe one a day, or one a week?

Application in a nutshell	What I will do, and when I will do it
1.	
2.	
3.	
4.	

Decide on a time to pray regularly for these needs, alone or with a prayer partner. "Ask and keep on asking, and it shall be given you" (Luke 11:9 AMP).

3. Now take fifteen minutes for prayer.
   - Praise God for the specific verses, truths and results you have recorded in Questions 3 and 5, pages 92 and 93.
   - Pray about the symptoms you wrote down in Question 1, page 94.
   - Pray about the items for prayer and action in Question 2 above.
   - Pray for several friends and loved ones, that in new ways they will trust God's goodness and submit to his plan for them.
   - Pray for opportunities to share with others some of the truths you have learned. Ask God to prepare hearts ahead of time, to give you graciousness and wisdom, and to use his word in life-changing ways.
   - Thank God for the privilege of giving yourself unreservedly to him; for the joy of knowing that his plan is for his greatest glory and your highest good now and forever; and for the security you have because he is controlling your circumstances and destiny, and is working *in you*. "Now to him who is able to do exceeding abundantly beyond all that we ask or think, according to the power that works within us, to Him be the glory in the church and in Christ Jesus to all generations forever and ever. Amen" (Ephesians 3:20-21).

Optional:

If you were to give a talk on God's Good Plan:

   a. What aspect of his plan would you choose?

   b. Jot down the specific purposes of your talk—how you want to influence your audience:

   —in how they think

   —in changed actions toward God or people

   c. What would be the main divisions of your talk?

   d. Choose one or more basic verses for each division.

   e. Find an illustration for each point, to clarify and motivate.

Notes and Quotes. *Add your own as you discover them.*

Samples:

Make Me Thy Fuel

From prayer that asks that I may be
Sheltered from winds that beat on Thee,
From fearing when I should aspire,
From faltering when I should climb higher,
From silken self, O Captain, free
Thy soldier who would follow Thee.

From subtle love of softening things,
From easy choices, weakenings,
(Not thus are spirits fortified,
Not this way went the Crucified)
From all that dims Thy Calvary
O Lamb of God, deliver me.

Give me the love that leads the way,
The faith that nothing can dismay,
The hope no disappointments tire,
The passion that will burn like fire;
Let me not sink to be a clod:
Make me Thy fuel, Flame of God.
                        —Amy Carmichael
                    Toward Jerusalem

We see in burning-glasses, where the beams of the sun meet in one, how forcible they are, because there is a union of the beams in a little point. Let it be our labour that all the beams of our love may meet in Christ, that He may be our Beloved. As all streams meet in the great ocean, so let all our loves meet in Christ. We cannot bestow our love and our affections better than upon Christ. It is a happiness that we have such affections as joy, delight, and love, planted in us by God; and what a happiness is it that we should have such an excellent Object to fill those affections, yea, to transcend, and more than satisfy them!
                                                    —Richard Sibbes

Giving God My Past

It is possible to drag our past like a heavy load through all the days of our future. We can let unhealed hurts or angers fester deep within us all our lives. Or we can know more and more of the healing, liberating touch of the Lord as we cooperate with him and follow the principles he has revealed in the Bible.

Prayerfully work through the sections below, asking the Lord for courage and honesty, enlightenment and release. Record your answers on a separate page.

1. *Review your past and your feelings about it.*
   * Think back over what has happened to you—your background, your parents and family, other people who have influenced you, the events and opportunities of your past life. Record anything about your past that hinders you today:

     a) the things or people you resent or are ashamed of,
     b) the things you are proud of or take credit for,
     c) the things you regret or condemn yourself for.

   * Write down your feelings about the things you have recorded, such as fear, anxiety, shame, humiliation, anger, hurt, rejection, abandonment, inferiority, pride, superiority, guilt. Before you write, take time to tune in to your deeper feelings. Step back inwardly from the clamor of your obvious emotions, or from your preconceived ideas of what you do or do not feel, and focus on your deep-down responses to what your past included. Your goal is not to scold or condemn yourself, for God has cancelled any and all guilt that may be involved—past, present, and future. You simply want to bring gently into the light anything that needs the Lord's loving, healing touch. So take time to listen, willing to accept whatever comes to your attention. Then be specific in writing down a description of each feeling.

2. *Let the Lord into your memories and feelings.*
   * From your list, select one past experience which is painful to remember.

   * Think back over the truths you have studied in this book. Record what you think the Lord would have said to you had he been physically present with you when that event happened.

   * Tell the Lord how you feel about that situation and how it has affected you. "Pour out your heart before Him" (Psalm 62:8).

   * Our imagination is a God-given faculty that we can use to experience God with greater reality. Imagine in detail the experience you have selected, picturing the place, the people, the sequence of events. Allow the feelings it

then aroused to arise within you now. Then envision the Lord beside you, taking your hand or putting his arm around your shoulder, telling you by expression and by word how he felt about that incident, and how he feels about you now. Wait and listen in his presence. Whenever the old feelings return, by faith visualize him again as he has revealed himself, letting his love and empathy fill your heart.

3. *Choose fresh, new attitudes and responses.*
   - You cannot change the past, but you do not need to keep sinking into your old feelings and reactions. You can let God loosen their hold upon you by your faith-choices today.

   - *Confess* to God any sin on your part that he brings to mind—such as an unforgiving spirit, resentment, or pride. Remember that he is with you not to condemn but to forgive you, to encourage you, and to embrace you warmly, as the father did the prodigal son in Luke 15.

   - *Choose to forgive* any people that you feel failed you, whether in your childhood or more recently. You may not feel like forgiving them, but decide to do so, asking the Lord to produce in you both the desire and the power to do his will (Philippians 2:13). Forgiveness does not mean to justify or condone another's behavior, but to let go of your feelings of anger or resentment about it. It means that you are ready to extend forgiveness if the other person comes to you some day and asks for it, and to put away your feelings about the person even if he never asks. If we do not forgive others, we cannot be freed from our past hurts and emotional scars. Forgiving them wholeheartedly means release and peace (Ephesians 4:31-32). Forgiveness that is genuine is the scalpel God uses to clean out old emotional wounds; it helps heal them and replace the scars with normal tissue.

   - *Choose to forgive yourself.* Sometimes forgiving others brings us face-to-face with personal guilt we formerly denied. It is essential to accept the fact that we are not the person we thought we were, and to forgive ourselves. Persistently practicing these three steps—receiving God's forgiveness through confession, forgiving the other person, and forgiving ourselves—helps cut away the ropes that bind us to the past and its hurts.

   Again, use your imagination. Visualize your resentment or anger (or fear, anxiety, or guilt) tied to the end of a heavy rope which is tightly wound around and around your feet, legs, arms, and shoulders, immobilizing you and chafing painfully when you try to move. Then picture Jesus coming to you, gently cutting away the rope so that you are loosed from the negative feelings, and applying soothing ointment that heals the chafed spots. Fall at his feet and thank him. "If . . . the Son shall make you free, you shall be free indeed" (John 8:36).

- *Decide* to accept the past event as part of the "all things" the Lord will work together for your good (Romans 8:28). This choice begins to bring in a positive attitude of acceptance in place of the old negative responses.

4. *Reinforce your new patterns of thought and feeling.*
   - Thank the Lord for the thing that happened. The attitude God desires us to adopt is found in 1 Thessalonians 5:18, "In everything give thanks; for this is God's will for you in Christ Jesus." Any response that falls short of this is unscriptural and nails our feet to the ground, hindering progress in his plan for us. The verse does not command us to *feel* thankful, but to *give* thanks. As we choose to do this, we open an avenue that lets God enter our feelings and eventually produce a sense of thankfulness. Thanksgiving provides a bulwark against the return of our feelings of resentment, regret, or self-glory.

   - Find a verse or truth you feel will help transform your thoughts and feelings and reinforce your new choices. Meditate upon it so that you experience a deepening sense of its truth. As the days pass, review it often with thanksgiving; and use it to displace the old negative feelings when they arise. Visualize again your experience of Jesus setting you free, and repeatedly thank God for doing so.

   - Continue to give thanks. Whenever any resentment recurs, immediately thank him for the event or person involved and for the benefits he plans to bring out of the past situation. When proud feelings return, thank him as the source of the ability or achievement about which you feel pride. When you begin to feel self-condemning, thank him that the thing you regret has been forgiven and erased from God's memory (Hebrews 8:12), and that he will use it for good in your life and in the lives of others. Your continued victory depends on keeping Jesus Christ central in your life. Thanksgiving helps to keep him there.

As you begin to open up before the Lord in this way, you may at first find yourself dealing with more-or-less surface memories and feelings. Continue praying over the above points for a period of time, giving the Lord a chance to clarify other things you should record and work through with him.

"Two are better than one" (Ecclesiastes 4:9). You may find it best to do all or part of the above points with someone else—a friend, spouse, pastor, or counsellor who would be understanding, someone who would support you and pray with and for you. "If two of you agree on earth about anything that they may ask, it shall be done for them by My Father who is in heaven. For where two or three have gathered together in My name, there I am in their midst" (Matthew 18:19-20).

These same helps can be used in handling our responses to our recent past—one year, one month, one hour ago—as well as our distant past.

All this takes time. But far more time is lost year after year if we do not resolve our unprofitable reactions to the past.

APPENDIX B
Finding God's Will

In your decisions, especially your major ones, the following principles can help you discover God's good, well-pleasing, and perfect will (see Romans 12:1-2).

For some years we have used this checklist with great profit. In major decisions such as getting engaged and going overseas as missionaries, we have gone over it in detail. Sometimes for several months we have kept a running record of light the Holy Spirit has given through these points, then prayerfully reviewed it as the time of decision approached. Other times we go over the list more rapidly.

We find that often the Lord doesn't use all the points. Sometimes he gives us one or two big 1000-watt lights. At other times he gives many small 50-watt ones that make us equally sure of his leading. If we come to yellow or red lights, we evaluate further, and generally wait for clarification.

To use this list more effectively we suggest that you record the light the Lord gives as you consider the principles. Arrange your information under "Pros" (positive factors and advantages), "Cons" (negative factors and disadvantages), and "Alternatives."

Pros	Cons	Alternatives

In emotionally loaded issues, such as courtship, marriage, or healing, seek to give greater weight to the more objective principles. Don't rely only on peace, verses that jump out at you, or personal desires and feelings.

PRINCIPLES IN FINDING GOD'S WILL

1. *Lordship*—Am I willing to do God's will, whatever it may be? This is the indispensable foundation for finding his will.
   Romans 12:1-2   Luke 9:23
2. *God's word*—What principles, commands, or prohibitions apply? Has he given me any motivating verses or promises on the subject?
   John 8:31-32   Psalm 119:130,105
3. *Prayer*—Have I prayed adequately about this? As I pray in a certain direction, do I have continued freedom in prayer, or lack of it?
   Philippians 4:6   James 1:5
4. *My God-given priorities, gifts, and calling*—What gifts and abilities has God given me, and how does he want me to use these to accomplish his purposes in the world? What course of action is most in line with the long-range inclinations he has built into me?
   Acts 20:24   Matthew 28:18-20   1 Corinthians 10:31-33
   Romans 12   1 Corinthians 12

5. *The Holy Spirit's continued inner promptings*—Does he motivate me toward or away from a particular course of action?
Psalm 143:10   Galatians 5:16   Romans 8:14

6. *Godly counsel*—What is the prayerful counsel of someone who knows me and is somewhat familiar with the situation? Am I avoiding or disregarding counsel that I should consider? What about parental counsel, especially if I am not yet of age?
Proverbs 19:20   Proverbs 15:22

7. *Providential circumstances*—Has God arranged events to point clearly in one direction? If I am facing obstacles, are they from God to stop me? Or are they satanic hindrances to be overcome by faith?
Revelation 3:7-8   Philippians 1:12-14   Romans 8:28

8. *Common sense and personal desires*—What does common sense tell me? What are my feelings and desires—and those of people close to me who will be affected by this decision? Which of these factors seem to be from God? Which seem to be temptations to make a wrong or second-best choice?
Psalm 37:4   1 John 2:15-16

9. *Peace*—Do I have continued inner peace as I consider these principles in prayer? Or do I experience restlessness, impatience, or inner conflict?
Colossians 3:15   1 John 3:21-22

10. *Timing*—What is God's mind about the *when* of this decision? Are my emotions pressing me to rush too fast? Or to hold back too long before stepping out— perhaps through fear, or by waiting too long for conclusive evidence?
Psalm 27:14   Lamentations 3:25   2 Corinthians 8:11

11. *Faith*—Does God want me to step out or halt by faith—trusting him to overrule if I make a sincere mistake, and to take care of all the consequences to myself and others of doing his will?
Psalm 37:5   Proverbs 3:5-6

SEEKING GUIDANCE THROUGH THE SCRIPTURES

In seeking guidance from God's word, we should give primary attention to the commands and principles for living that apply to all believers. Occasionally God guides us (or confirms guidance already given) by impressing us with a verse that seems tailor-made for our situation. This is a valid form of guidance. But we must recognize the subjective element in it, avoiding the possible dangers of relying on it too much, and refrain from being dogmatic about our conclusions. We should ask ourselves:

Is this God speaking, or am I merely finding confirmation for what I want? (It is possible to make the Scriptures say things we desire, and to ignore passages that give other light.)

Do other avenues of finding God's will (such as my own willingness, scriptural principles, continued prayer, and godly counsel) confirm my impressions or throw doubt on their accuracy?

Do I approach the Bible looking for verses to leap out at me and so miss the overall teachings of the word and personal fellowship with the living God?

Do I use this as an easy method of finding God's will, a Christian substitute for horoscopes and Ouija boards, in place of carefully determining what he wants and making mature decisions?

Sometimes people find promises and interpret them as specific assurances about the future; then, when things do not turn out as they expect, they become disillusioned, perhaps even doubting the Bible's trustworthiness. They fail to realize that they have simply misinterpreted what God said and misclaimed the promise. This need not be humiliating—even the apostle Paul occasionally mistook God's will (see page 85, Optional Question). Our mistakes can remind us not to force the Bible into saying what we want to hear. It can spur us to approach the Scriptures with the primary purpose of knowing God better and learning to see things as he does, so that we can walk in *his* ways.

> *Happy are we to have God's Word always to guide us! What were the mariner without his compass? And what were the Christian without the Bible? This is the unerring chart, the map in which every shoal is described, and all the channels from the quicksands of destruction to the haven of salvation mapped and marked by One who knows all the way.*
> —C.H. Spurgeon

SPECTACULAR GUIDANCE

God can, and sometimes does, guide in miraculous or spectacular ways—as by the angel and sheet and voice from heaven in Acts 10. But this is an exceptional occurrence, not the usual, basic way God guides people. If God chooses a spectacular method we surely will not miss it! Whereas if we constantly seek spectacular or dramatic guidance, we are likely to miss the enrichment and intimacy that come as we daily tune in to his word, his Spirit and his usual ways of communicating his will.

Elisabeth Elliot, in *A Slow and Certain Light*, made the following observations about guidance by miraculous means:

> *But there is one thing we ought to notice about these miracles. When God guided by means of the pillar of cloud and fire, by the star of Bethlehem, by visitations of angels, by the word coming through visions and dreams and prophets and even through an insulted donkey, in most cases these were not signs that had been asked for. And when they were asked for, as in the case of Jehoshaphat and Ahab, they were not accepted.*

> *Supernatural phenomena were given at the discretion of the divine wisdom. It is not for us to ask that God will guide us in some miraculous way. If, in his wisdom, he knows that such means are what we need, he will surely give them.*

APPENDIX C
Verses from Other Translations

STUDY 1—I CAN TRUST GOD'S PLAN

Psalm 103:5 BERK
Who satisfies you throughout life with good things, so that your youth is renewed like the eagle's.

Isaiah 48:17-18 NIV
This is what the Lord says—your Redeemer, the Holy One of Israel: "I am the Lord your God, who teaches you what is best for you, who directs you in the way you should go. If only you had paid attention to my commands, your peace would have been like a river, your righteousness like the waves of the sea."

Psalm 94:19 NASB
When my anxious thoughts multiply within me, Thy consolations delight my soul.

Jeremiah 32:40-41 BERK
And I will make an everlasting covenant with them, that I will not turn away from doing good to them; and My reverence will I put in their heart that they may not turn away from Me. I will rejoice over doing them good, and I will plant them in this land in faithfulness with all My heart and with all My soul.

Ephesians 1:8 LB
And he has showered down upon us the richness of his grace—for how well he understands us and knows what is best for us at all times.

1 John 4:18 LB
We need have no fear of someone who loves us perfectly; his perfect love for us eliminates all dread of what he might do to us. If we are afraid, it is for fear of what he might do to us, and shows that we are not fully convinced that he really loves us.

STUDY 2—I CANNOT TRUST MY PLANS

Deuteronomy 28:65-67 BERK
Among those nations you shall have no ease, nor shall you find a resting place for the sole of your foot. There the Lord will give you a trembling heart, homesick eyes, and a languishing spirit; you will sense danger night and day, your life in suspense, having no life security whatever. In the morning you shall say, 'O that it were evening!' and in the evening you shall say, 'O that it were morning!' because of the dread weariness of soul which you will experience, and the spectacle before your eyes.

Jeremiah 17:5-6 BERK
Thus says the Lord: Cursed is the man who trusts in man and makes flesh his arm, whose heart departs from the Lord. He is like a juniper tree in a desert and shall not be aware when good comes; he shall inhabit the parched places in the wilderness, an uninhabited salt land.

Ephesians 4:17-18 PH
This is my instruction then, which I give you in the Lord's name. Do not live any longer the futile lives of gentiles. For they live in a world of shadows, and are cut off from the life of God through their deliberate ignorance of mind and sheer hardness of heart.

Galatians 6:7-8 PH
Don't be under any illusion; you cannot make a fool of God! A man's harvest in life will depend entirely on what he sows. If he sows for his own lower nature his harvest will be the decay and death of his own nature.

STUDY 3— GOD CAN FULFILL HIS PLANS

Daniel 2:20-21 LB
Blessed be the name of God forever, for he alone has all wisdom and all power. World events are under his control. He removes kings and sets others on their thrones. He gives wise men their wisdom, and scholars their intelligence.

Proverbs 16:33 AMP
The lot is cast into the lap, but the decision is wholly of the Lord—even the events [that seem accidental] are really ordered by Him.

1 Peter 1:7 PH
This is no accident—it happens to prove your faith, which is infinitely more valuable than gold, and gold, as you know, even though it is ultimately perishable, must be purified by fire.

Ephesians 1:19-21 PH
That power is the same divine energy which was demonstrated in Christ when he raised him from the dead and gave him the place of highest honour in Heaven—a place that is infinitely superior to any command, authority, power or control, and which carries with it a name far beyond any name that could ever be used in this world or the world to come.

Isaiah 30:18 RSV
Therefore the Lord waits to be gracious to you; therefore he exalts himself to show mercy to you. For the Lord is a God of justice; blessed are all who wait for him.

STUDY 4—WHY GOD INCLUDES TRIALS

James 1:2-5 PH
When all kinds of trials and temptations crowd into your lives, my brothers, don't resent them as intruders, but welcome them as friends! Realize that they come to test your faith and to produce in you the quality of endurance. But let the process go on until that endurance is fully developed, and you will find you have become men of mature character, men of integrity with no weak spots. And if, in the process, any of you does not know how to meet any particular problem he has only to ask God—who gives generously to all men without making them feel guilty—and he may be quite sure that the necessary wisdom will be given him.

Romans 5:2-5 LB
For because of your faith, he has brought us into this place of highest privilege where we now stand, and we confidently and joyfully look forward to actually becoming all that God has had in mind for us to be. We can rejoice, too, when we run into problems and trials, for we know that they are good for us—they help us learn to be patient. And patience develops strength of character in us and helps us trust God more each time we use it until finally our hope and faith are strong and steady. Then, when that happens, we are able to hold our heads high no matter what happens and know that all is well, for we know how dearly God loves us, and we feel this warm love everywhere within us because God has given us the Holy Spirit to fill our hearts with his love.

Romans 8:29 LB
For from the very beginning God decided that those who came to him—and all along he knew who would—should become like his Son, so that his Son would be the First, with many brothers.

Psalm 94:12-13 BERK
Blessed is the man whom Thou dost discipline, whom Thou dost instruct from Thy Law, O Lord, that he may enjoy security during the days of distress, till a pit be dug for the wicked.

Hebrews 12:2-3 BERK
With our eyes on Jesus, the Cause and Completer of our faith who, in view of the joy that lay ahead for Him, submitted to the cross, thought little of the shame, and is seated at the right hand of the throne of God. Compare your experience with His, Who was willing to stand so much contradicting from the sinners against Himself, so that your souls may not wear out from despondency.

STUDY 5—GOD'S PLAN AND WHO I AM

Psalm 139:13-14 LB
You made all the delicate, inner parts of my body, and knit them together in my

mother's womb. Thank you for making me so wonderfully complex! It is amazing to think about. Your workmanship is marvelous—and how well I know it.

Ephesians 1:11 LB
Moreover, because of what Christ has done we have become gifts to God that he delights in, for as part of God's sovereign plan we were chosen from the beginning to be his, and all things happen just as he decided long ago.

Isaiah 29:16 RSV
You turn things upside down! Shall the potter be regarded as the clay; that the thing made should say of its maker, "He did not make me"; or the thing formed say of him who formed it, "He has no understanding"?

2 Corinthians 4:6-7 NIV
For God, who said, "Let light shine out of darkness," made his light shine in our hearts to give us the light of the knowledge of the glory of God in the face of Christ. But we have this treasure in jars of clay ("in a common earthenware jar" PH) to show that this all-surpassing power is from God and not from us.

Galatians 2:6 AMP
Moreover, [no new requirements were made] by those who were reputed to be something, though what was their individual position and whether they really were of importance or not makes no difference to me; God is not impressed with the positions that men hold and He is not partial and recognizes no external distinctions.

STUDY 6—GOD'S PLAN AND MY PAST

Psalm 139:16 LB
You saw me before I was born and scheduled each day of my life before I began to breathe. Every day was recorded in your Book!

Romans 11:33-34 PH
I stand amazed at the fathomless wealth of God's wisdom and God's knowledge. How could man ever understand his reasons for action, or explain his methods of working? For: Who hath known the mind of the Lord? Or who hath been his counsellor?

Exodus 3:7, 16 NASB
And the Lord said, "I have surely seen the affliction of My people who are in Egypt, and have given heed to their cry because of their taskmasters, for I am aware of their sufferings . . . . I am indeed concerned about you and what has been done to you in Egypt."

Romans 8:1, 33-34 PH
The truth is that no condemnation now hangs over the head of those who are "in" Christ Jesus . . . . Who would dare to accuse us, whom God has chosen? God

himself has declared us free from sin. Who is in a position to condemn? Only Christ Jesus, and Christ died for us, Christ also rose for us, Christ reigns in power for us, Christ prays for us!

James 1:9-10 WMS
Let the poor brother of lowly station rejoice in his exalted station as a Christian, and the rich brother rejoice in his being on a level with the poor . . . .

STUDY 7—GOD'S PLAN FOR MY DEVELOPMENT

Philippians 1:6 LB
And I am sure that God who began the good work within you will keep on helping you grow in his grace until his task within you is finally finished on that day when Jesus Christ returns.

Jude 24 LB
And he is able to keep you from slipping and falling away, and to bring you, sinless and perfect, into his glorious presence with mighty shouts of everlasting joy.

STUDY 8—GOD'S PLAN AND MY FUTURE

Psalm 31:14-15 HAR
But I have complete confidence in You, Lord, for I have said, 'You are my God. My destiny is under Your Control.'

Psalm 62:1-2, 7 MOF
Leave it all quietly to God, my soul, my rescue comes from Him alone; rock, rescue, refuge, He is all to me, never shall I be overthrown . . . my safety and my honor rest on God.

Philippians 4:13 AMP
I have strength for all things in Christ Who empowers me—I am ready for anything and equal to anything through Him Who infuses inner strength into me, [that is, I am self-sufficient in Christ's sufficiency].

2 Thessalonians 1:8-10 PH
This judgment will issue in the final appearance of the Lord Jesus from Heaven with the angels of his power. He will bring full justice in dazzling flame upon those who have refused to recognize God or to obey the gospel of our Lord Jesus. Their punishment will be eternal loss—exclusion from the radiance of the face of the Lord, and the glorious majesty of his power. But to those whom he has made holy his coming will mean splendour unimaginable. It will be a breath-taking wonder to all who believe—including you, for you have believed the message that we have given you.

Romans 8:16-18 PH
The Spirit himself endorses our inward conviction that we really are the children of God. Think what that means. If we are his children then we are God's heirs, and all that Christ inherits will belong to all of us as well! Yes, if we share in his sufferings we shall certainly share in his glory. In my opinion whatever we may have to go through now is less than nothing compared with the magnificent future God has in store for us.

STUDY 9—GOD'S PLAN AND WHY I AM HERE

1 Corinthians 2:7 NIV
No, we speak of God's secret wisdom, a wisdom that has been hidden and that God destined for our glory before time began.

STUDY 10—GOD'S PLAN AND MY RESPONSE

Psalm 147:11 LB
But his joy is in those who reverence him, those who expect him to be loving and kind.

Isaiah 41:10, 13 NASB
Do not fear, for I am with you; do not anxiously look about you, for I am your God. I will strengthen you, surely I will help you, surely I will uphold you with My righteous right hand . . . For I am the Lord your God, who upholds your right hand, Who says to you, "Do not fear, I will help you."

STUDY 11—GOD'S ASSURED GUIDANCE

Galatians 5:25 LB
If we are living now by the Holy Spirit's power, let us follow the Holy Spirit's leading in every part of our lives.

Romans 12:2 PH
Don't let the world around you squeeze you into its own mould, but let God re-make you so that your whole attitude of mind is changed. Thus you will prove in practice that the will of God is good, acceptable to him and perfect. (But be transformed [changed] by the [entire] renewal of your mind—by its new ideals and its new attitude . . . AMP).

Proverbs 16:3 NIV
Commit to the Lord whatever you do, and your plans will succeed.

Romans 12:17-18 NASB
Respect [take thought for] what is right in the sight of all men. If possible, so far as it depends on you, be at peace with all men.

FOR FURTHER READING

Johnston, Russ. *How to Know the Will of God*. Colorado Springs, Colorado: NavPress, 1976.
Little, Paul E. *Affirming the Will of God*. Downers Grove, Illinois: Inter-Varsity Press, 1979.

The following biographies provide illustrations of truths covered in *Discovering God's Will:*

Elliot, Elisabeth. *Through Gates of Splendor*. Old Tappan, New Jersey: Fleming H. Revell, 1979.
Pollock, John. *Hudson Taylor and Maria*. Grand Rapids, Michigan: Zondervan Publishing House, 1979.
Skinner, Betty Lee. *Daws*. Grand Rapids, Michigan: Zondervan Publishing House, 1974.
Steer, Roger. *George Müller: Delighted in God*. Wheaton, Illinois: Harold Shaw Publishers, 1979.